Paragraph Development in Writing English Research Papers

英文研究論文寫作
段落指引

國立臺灣師範大學翻譯研究所　副教授　**廖柏森** 博士　著
臺灣翻譯學學會　理事

眾文圖書 股份 有限 公司

「有知有覺」的學習撰寫英文研究論文

　　以當今國際化的趨勢，以英文寫作論文達到知識及研究成果與全球共享的目的，是每個碩博士生必經的學習過程，以個人過去指導研究生寫論文的經驗，常常發現同學在口頭討論的時候，想法非常好，很有創意，也具研究的學術價值，但訴諸文字時卻經常詞不達意，或者組織不合邏輯，或者篇章安排不當，因而無法將原本很有創意的研究重點清楚表達。廖柏森教授的大作《英文研究論文寫作——段落指引》的出版，正可幫助抒解此困境，極符合國內廣大碩博士學術寫作的需求。

　　本書主要的特色之一是兼顧英文論文寫作的宏觀及微觀層面，歸納一篇論文該有的結構區塊，讓讀者既有整篇文章的面貌，又可將整篇論文各個擊破，形成多個有意義的語塊以掌握文章撰寫的脈絡。全書除前言外，包含摘要、緒論、研究方法、研究結果及討論，儼然一篇學術論文該有的組織架構，而且每個部分還包含章節的細節發展。每個章節以解說開始，佐以在期刊論文精選的範例，每個範例均附有中文翻譯，及逐句的句型、文法重點和用字遣詞的講解，接著則是抽離內容的句型以凸顯區塊的架構，最後讓讀者練習填寫自己的研究內容，組合成篇，立即練習回饋。

　　本書另一特色是在句型及詞彙的練習上以詞彙群的概念來安排講解，符合當代認知語言學派所強調的學習理念，即在一定的認知框架下以語意群組的方式學習，無論是對文本的理解或者產出均較有助益。全書即遵循這樣的模式安排，將論文篇章的結構性區塊詳細分析講解後，讓讀者填入個別學術領域的內容，反覆在整體論文架構及章節細節之間

來回練習反芻以求熟練。誠言，「像不像三分樣」，只要按著本書的安排循序漸進反覆練習，必能舉一反三，熟稔論文寫作的技巧，並能將想法清楚表達，寫好一篇英文研究論文。

總之，本書符合當今英文學術論文之寫作需求，讓讀者「有知有覺」的學習撰寫流暢而正確的英文研究論文，是一本值得推薦的好書。

國立政治大學英國語文學系特聘教授

為研究生、大學教師提供指引的論文寫作專書

很高興看到廖柏森老師的新書《英文研究論文寫作——段落指引》的出版。這本書整合廖老師前三本英文研究論文寫作系列：《英文研究論文寫作——關鍵句指引》、《英文研究論文寫作——搭配詞指引》及《英文研究論文寫作——文法指引》，整個系列提供研究生在論文寫作時從摘要、緒論、研究方法、研究結果、討論，乃至於致謝等不同章節之寫作範例及練習。此書更以段落為單位，深入探討論文各部分的結構、用字遣詞，及可替換之不同語詞，讓初次嘗試寫研究論文之學生能由模仿習作漸漸掌握研究論文寫作的訣竅。

對於寫研究報告的新手而言，要構思研究主題、設計研究方法、收集資料、分析結果等研究過程，其工程已十分艱鉅，要再把整個過程詳實記載、分析，並撰寫成完整且易讀的研究報告誠屬不易，但所幸研究論文有其既定格式及應有的章節，每一章節也有其慣用的鋪陳方式，甚至連語言結構也有章法可循，初學者如能依循此脈絡，一定可以將自己的研究清楚陳述。廖老師的這一系列書即是為指引學生寫研究論文而規畫、撰寫的。

廖老師在本書前言中提到近十年來台灣的碩博士研究生人數暴增，因此研究論文寫作的需求也與日俱增，不僅如此，現在大學之間彼此競爭激烈，許多大學也要求大學部學生要寫畢業論文，科技大學也多會要求學生寫專題報告，因此本書不但對研究生寫研究論文有莫大幫助，對大學生的畢業論文、專題報告也能提供指引。除了學生寫論文的需求外，各大專院校對於教師的研究能量也十分關注，尤其是在國際期刊發

表的能量更是各校教師專業成長的指標，因此本書也提供了擬發表於國際期刊的國內學者一塊敲門磚，得以深入了解刊登於國際學術期刊之論文其文字架構上的共通點。

　　本書特色在於它提供了一個「版型 (template)」，讓每個研究者可以依自己研究內容套入一個已約定俗成的論文架構中，因此寫論文時只要有內容，只要英語文字表達清晰、流暢，就不必擔心論文結構是否符合規格，是否易於閱讀及理解。這是一本撰寫英文論文時必備的工具書，非常值得推薦！

國立臺灣師範大學英語學系教授

陳秋蘭

前言

　　英文研究論文寫作在學術競爭全球化的今日非常重要，而台灣的研究者在這方面的表現向來不俗。我國的國家實驗研究院科技政策研究中心曾做過分析，以 National Science Indicators 資料庫搜尋國際學術論文，顯示台灣學者在 2009 年共發表 24,305 篇論文，在全球約 150 個國家中排名第 16 名，論文數量的能見度相當高。而以論文的品質而言，我國的成績也不錯，從 2005 到 2009 年的五年期間，共被引用 337,133 次，全球排名第 19 名。當然整體來說，這樣的研究成績還可以再精益求精、更上一層。但從另一方面，也就是剛加入研究社群的研究生來看，其英文論文寫作的表現就難免令人憂心。主因在於國內研究生的數量於近年內激增，可是目前學生的程度和學校投入的教學資源都不符預期，值得國內高等教育學界注意。

　　據內政部統計，截至 2009 年底，國人擁有碩、博士學歷的人數已提升至 86 萬人，在十年間劇增了四倍。而教育部的資料也顯示，在 89 年度，全國博士班共有 450 所 13,822 人，碩士班有 1,397 所 70,039 人；而到了 99 年度，博士班增為 794 所 33,751 人，碩士班則增至 3,303 所 183,401 人。也就是說，過去十年間，博士班大幅成長 344 所 19,929 人，而碩士班更暴增了 1,906 所 113,362 人。高等研究人才的增長幅度可謂驚人，如果能夠好好加以訓練指導，這將是提高我國研究能量的大好契機，而其中英文能力就扮演關鍵的角色。研究生除了必須以英文獲取國際間最新研究資訊和理論知識，也常需要以英文寫作來傳達其研究的成果，按理對於研究生英文程度的要求也應愈高。不過目前研究所因數量激增，導致入學門檻降低，研究生的英文普遍欠佳，而學校當局卻常誤以為研究所不需要再訓練英文，很少針對研究生開設英文課程，導致大量的研究社群潛力無法完全發揮，極為可惜。

　　筆者現於研究所任教，也長期教授英文論文寫作，深知國內研究生在英文寫作上的困境與需求，覺得各大學對研究生英文學習的關注不夠，因此過去幾年來一直致力於編寫一系列英文研究論文寫作的專書，希望能稍微彌補一下學校教育資源的不足，也有幸得到廣大讀者的迴響。之前出版的三本論文寫作專書：《英文研究論文寫作——關鍵句指引》、《英文研究論文寫作——搭配詞指引》、《英文研究論文寫作——文法指引》，內容涵蓋英文句型、用字和文法的重點，都已分別付梓再刷數版。

◉ 本書的內容和特色

　　而本書《英文研究論文寫作——段落指引》則是整合之前三本著作，而且進一步結合語意邏輯、用字遣詞和篇章架構的發展，提供段落寫作和標點用法的指引，兼顧英文論文寫作的宏觀與微觀層面，每種語意段落的編排分為（一）**範例**：精選學術期刊論文的英文段落作為範例並附上中文翻譯；（二）**講解**：逐句講解範例段落中的句型特色、文法重點和重要詞彙用法；（三）**句型**：把原文的研究內容抽離，提供句型的架構，呈顯語意的邏輯發展與句型架構的關係；（四）**練習**：只呈現句型架構，讓讀者以填入空格的方式來練習段落寫作。另外書後約四分之一篇幅則介紹論文寫作中常見標點符號的用法和練習，包括逗號、句號、分號、冒號、引號、撇號、破折號、連字號、圓括號和方括號等，讓讀者對一些習以為常但其實容易犯錯的標點符號用法有進一步的理解。

　　本書的主要特色在於把論文段落視為多個意義語塊或詞組的組合，進而形成連貫的篇章。而且組合的方式往往可歸納成幾種常用模式，以有效率地傳達論文內容的訊息。此種觀點源自於 Lewis (2002)

所提倡的詞語教學法 (lexical approach)，他主張語言通常是由多字的預製語塊 (multi-word prefabricated chunks) 所構成；換句話說，現行的語言文字都是由之前使用過的多種詞組所生成。因此教學的重點應該放在我們經常使用的詞語組合上，而不是致力於創造新的句子。本書採取相同的立場，大量蒐集已在國際期刊上發表過的英文論文，擷取各章節中有代表性的語意段落，加以詳細的解說分析，並整理出常用的句型模式，供讀者練習論文段落的寫作。不過由於原論文的段落相當長，又牽涉到不同領域的專業知識，對本書讀者幫助不大，因此筆者的工作還包括簡化改寫原論文的內容並縮短段落長度，但保留了段落的主要結構和重要用字，希望有利於讀者學習上的便利。另需加說明的是，因為改寫過的段落和原文差異過大，已幾乎不屬直接引用的範圍，因此並未在每個段落加註資料來源。但讀者若對原文出處有興趣，請直接參閱書後的參考書目 (References)，內有詳細的文獻出處。

這些段落的解說基本上與我在課堂上教授論文寫作課時的內容雷同。當我在課堂上教導學生如何寫作時，都會使用已經在國際期刊出版的論文段落作為範例，提醒同學注意多從上下文語境 (context) 的關係來理解詞組的意義，並歸納結構相同的詞組，以提高他們對詞組搭配型式的意識 (awareness)，進而習得其中字詞標點的用法、句法的結構組織、意義的鋪陳轉折等要點。而這本書就是把我上課口語講解的內容轉化為書面文字與讀者分享，因此本書除了可放在案頭供查詢參考之用外，從教學的觀點出發，也可作為國內大學院校在英文論文寫作課中使用的教材。本書已把論文段落的基本架構建立好，教師可以段落為單位來教導用字和文法功能，之後並請同學按架構練習段落寫作。當然讀者亦可自修本書，多次練習段落中的句型寫作之後，甚至可舉一反三，自行創製新的語意段落，以收事半功倍之效。

● 套用句型並非抄襲

另外值得一提的是，筆者過去在各大學和研究機構演講英文論文寫作時，偶爾有聽眾問到，使用別人期刊論文上的句型會不會構成抄襲 (plagiarism) 的問題？我們在此可以做個釐清。首先看一下《韋氏大學辭典》(*Merriam-Webster's Collegiate Dictionary*) 對抄襲的定義爲：to commit literary theft: present as new and original an idea or product derived from an existing source（著述上的盜竊：從現存來源衍生，卻以全新獨創的觀念或作品呈現）。而研究論文的常用句型從未被視爲是全新或獨創的元素，只有研究的結果和內容才需要凸顯其原創性，這也才是會構成抄襲的部分。再者，美國著名的論文寫作教科書 *Academic Writing for Graduate Students* 作者 Swales 和 Feak (2004:172) 在這本書中也提到：Of course, borrowing the words and phrases of others can be a useful language learning strategy. Certainly you would not be plagiarizing if you borrowed items that are commonly or frequently used in academic English or that are part of common knowledge.（向別人借用字彙或片語當然是種有用的語言學習策略，如果你借用的是在學術英文中常用的項目或常識，絕對不算是抄襲。）而且他們還舉出幾個句型如 The results from this experiment seem to suggest that...（實驗結果似乎指出……）和 These results are statistically significant.（這些結果具統計上的顯著性。）等都是借用的例子，在寫作學習策略上還可以稱之爲平行文本 (parallel text)。

再從針對學術寫作 (academic writing) 本身的研究來看，上述的常用句型有學者稱爲 lexical bundles（詞彙群）（如 Biber, Johansson, Leech, Conrad & Finegan, 1999），也有人稱之爲 chunks（語塊）（如 Lewis, 2000, 2002）或 cluster （詞組）（如 Scott, 1996）。無論名稱爲

何，它們都是指「詞彙組合的頻率是高於隨機的預期，而有助於釐清文本語意以及我們對特定語域的了解」(words which follow each other more frequently than expected by chance, helping to shape text meanings and contribute to our sense of distinctiveness in a register [Hyland, 2008:42])。而且研究結果也指出，愈成熟的作者就愈常使用這些詞彙搭配的型式 (Haswell, 1991)，而學習某一研究領域的固定詞組，就能提升在該領域的溝通能力 (Hyland, 2008)。

換個方式來說，研究論文其實也是由許多語塊或詞組所合成，依其功能大體上可分為內容性語塊 (content-oriented chunks) 和結構性語塊 (organization-oriented chunks)。內容性語塊用來表達每個學術領域不同的研究主題、知識內容和細節資訊，每個人精心研究的內容應該不會一樣；而結構性語塊則主要是用來銜接、連貫、延展、總結或概括研究論文的內容，是種組織語意的架構或框架 (frame)，大部分的研究論文都會遵循類似的結構來撰寫。尤其研究論文是種極為正式嚴謹的文體，而從文體學的觀點來看，愈正式的文體，其文體結構和語言特點就愈客觀明確，也就愈容易辨識和歸納出眾所遵循的模式或架構。因此對於初學英文論文寫作者而言，了解論文不同章節段落中的常用句型模式，進而加以模擬練習，應當會有很大的助益。

如果還是有人質疑句型雷同的問題，我們換個角度從中文論文寫作來做個對比就會更清楚，例如某一作者的原句是：

「本研究旨在探討電腦輔助教學在國內英語教學上的應用。」

而以下兩個改寫的句子中，哪個句子看起來比較像抄襲原句呢？

(1)「此研究的目的在於探究**電腦輔助教學**在**國內英語教學**上的使
用。」

(2)「**本研究旨在探討**學生學習策略**在**英語課堂**上的應用。**」

可能大多數人會認爲第 (1) 句比較像抄襲，爲什麼呢？因爲第 (1)
句與原句的內容語塊如「電腦輔助教學」和「國內英語教學」是一樣
的，難免會讓人聯想其他研究內容也會雷同，而這並不是本書提供指引
的寫法和教學立場。相對地，第 (2) 句與原句相同之處是結構性語塊如
「本研究旨在探討……在……上的應用。」每個人都可以使用這樣的句
型來表達各自不同的研究內容，也比較不會引起爭議。但就算還有人擔
心這樣仍有抄襲的可能性，那其實連結構性語塊也可以改寫，例如改成
「**此研究的目的在於探究**學生學習策略**在**英語課堂**上的使用。**」這句的結構
和原句都是一樣的，兩句皆在講「這個研究的目的在探討<u>某研究主題</u>在
<u>某領域或場所</u>的使用情況。」但這兩句的內容和用字都完全不同，沒有
人會認爲是抄襲。而這樣的寫作觀念和做法即爲本書的理論立場與操作
方式。

◉ 模仿句型有助提升寫作的效率

其實無論我們用中文或英文寫作論文時都會有一些慣用的固定或半
固定句型，每個人都可以使用，沒有抄襲的問題。而且筆者所謂的句型
架構並不是指具體特定的字詞組合，而是一個抽象的概念，只要用對了
正確架構就能有效傳達作者的旨意 (intended meaning)，至於構成此架
構的字詞是可以靈活代換、有許多變化的。只是我們在台灣用非母語的
英文寫作時心裡比較不踏實，覺得不是自己絞盡腦汁想出來的句子就有
點心虛，或者覺得使用別人寫過的句型沒有原創性。但其實除了文學創
作講究表達型式的創新之外，我們大部分的寫作還是在重複前人早已用

過的句型和用字。尤其學術論文寫作的重點是在內容上呈現創新的研究結果或理論，但文字表達基本上還是遵循共同的行文規範，常用的句型也相當一致，這樣才能促進學術社群在論文寫作和閱讀上的效率。因此學習模仿已經出版的國際期刊論文的句型和表達方式就不失為一種有效的捷徑。

當然筆者也要提醒讀者注意，此書提供的各種段落句構只是一種寫作的可能性，它們是描述性 (descriptive)，而不是規範性 (prescriptive) 的；亦即本書旨在描述分析國際期刊出版過的論文寫作文本，但並不是規定讀者都必須要如此寫作。本書的內容可讓初學英文論文寫作者在練習時有個可以依循的引導，有個可以支撐的架構，應該比一個人悶著頭拚命寫論文，結果反而創造出一大堆中式英文 (Chinglish) 的句型要來得有效。而且本書的引導和架構是開放的，也鼓勵讀者在符合英文語意的架構下去發揮自己的寫作才能，靈活運用，開展出最有效率的方式來傳達研究內容。

本書提出的學習論文寫作方式還可以用蓋大樓來作比喻，在興建過程中要建置鷹架 (scaffold) 來支持整棟建築物，本書的段落範例就有如鷹架支撐起你的研究內容；等大樓蓋到接近完工的階段就可以慢慢拆除掉鷹架，讓建築物自行挺立起來。或者我們再用另外一個比喻，就好像初學書法者，大多從臨摹字帖開始，會比自己摸索如何一筆一劃書寫更有效率。等反覆臨摹到某個階段，寫出的字體形神皆肖，漸次就可以自創新局，揮毫出個人的風格章法，也就不再需要依賴字帖了。而讀者使用本書的段落範例後，也應該會逐漸培養出自己撰寫論文的語感和風格，熟練之後自然就不再需要本書的指引。因此筆者編寫本書的長遠理想目標，就是期許讀者未來不用再參考本書也能寫出流暢正確的英文研

究論文；但是在那天來臨之前，也希望本書仍能作為讀者在學習論文寫作征途上最佳的夥伴。

國立臺灣師範大學翻譯研究所副教授

廖柏森

Contents

段落指引

Abstract 摘要 21

Introduction 緒論 33

標點指引

段落指引

Abstract

目前每個研究領域出版的論文數量都相當龐大,讀者通常會先檢索資料庫或電子期刊上提供的論文摘要,來判斷是否符合其需求並繼續閱讀全文,以節省尋找和參閱論文所需的時間和精力。另外,現在國內外學術研討會議大多只審查摘要以決定要不要接受研究者來發表論文,可見摘要的功能非常重要。而如何在眾多論文中脫穎而出,關鍵除了研究本身的品質之外,也在於是否能將摘要撰寫得精要明確,將全文的內容重點與邏輯關係在簡短的篇幅內陳述清楚,有效吸引讀者或審查委員的青睞。而一篇寫得好的摘要,通常也會讓人預期接下來應該就會讀到一篇好的論文。

論文摘要雖然是置於論文的最前頁,但在實際撰寫的順序上卻通常是在最後。也就是說,多數人都是在完成論文全文後才開始寫摘要,如此寫作時才能觀照全局而擷取必要的元素 (elements) 來組成摘要。

簡單而言,摘要是論文的精簡型式,摘要寫作的元素要包含全文的重要章節,也就是 Introduction(緒論)、Method(研究方法)、Results(研究結果)和 Discussion and Conclusions(討論/結論)中的精要訊息,不宜寫論文中從未提到的資訊。但畢竟摘要的字數有限制,如果是期刊論文摘要通常規定一段約兩三百字之內,而學位論文摘要則可寫到一至兩頁數段的結構。但摘要與全文相較都只是一小部分,因此要從全文中選擇何種資訊元素寫到摘要中就很重要。通常我們會依據摘要的字數規定和內容的重要性,選擇研究的背景 (background)、目的 (purpose)、方法 (method)、結果 (results) 或結論 (conclusions) 等元素寫到摘要中。

請看以下兩則期刊論文摘要的範例：

範例 1

此範例相當精簡，只有三句就分別把研究主題、研究缺口、研究的目的和方法交待清楚。雖然此範例並未明確寫出研究結果，但從其研究目的中即可看出作者所要獲得的成果。

---

① Many students need to learn how to give oral presentations, and there is a great deal of general literature on their preparation. ② There is little specific guidance, however, on how students can use language to signal their intentions. ③ Using a group of undergraduate students as an example, this paper will argue that the clause relational analysis developed by Hoey and Winter (1986) can provide a framework for oral presentations, as well as giving them greater cohesion, and a method of analyzing their effectiveness.

許多學生需要學習如何進行口語報告，而目前已有大量的一般性文獻研究學生如何準備報告。但是特定引導學生使用語言來指出意圖的研究卻很少。本文以一群大學部學生為例，主張 Hoey 和 Winter (1986) 所發展的子句關係分析法可作為口語報告的架構，並增進報告的連貫性，以及分析其成效的方式。

範例1 講解

1 Many students need to learn how to give oral presentations, <u>and</u> there is <u>a great deal of</u> general literature <u>on</u> their preparation.

- 第 1 句由兩個子句組成，第一個子句先指出研究的主題，亦即學習口語報告，再用對等連接詞 and 連接第二個子句。

- 第二個子句則說明目前的研究文獻多集中在一般性的論述 (general literature)，為下一個句子留下伏筆。

- 形容「大量」的文獻時，除了可以用 a great deal of 外，也可代換成 a considerable amount of, a good deal of, a significant body of, a vast amount of 等片語。

- literature（文獻）之後的介系詞用 on，表示是何種領域的文獻。

2 There is little specific guidance, <u>however</u>, on how students can use language to signal their intentions.

- 第 2 句指出研究的缺口 (research gap) 在於以前只有一般性 (general) 論述，所以目前需要特定性 (specific) 的研究。

- 表「然而」的連接副詞 (conjunctive adverb) however 除了置於句中，也可以置於句首形成 However, there is little specific guidance on...。however 還可代換成 nevertheless, nonetheless 等連接副詞。

3 Using a group of undergraduate students as an example, this paper will argue that the clause relational analysis developed by Hoey and Winter (1986) can provide a framework for oral presentations, as well as giving them greater cohesion, and a method of analyzing their effectiveness.

- 第 3 句撰寫此次的研究，等於是論文中的研究目的和方法，句子相當長。

- 首先使用現在分詞構句 Using... 指出研究的對象是大學生，主要子句主詞 this paper 之後再包含一個名詞子句 that... 作動詞 argue 的受詞，提出研究所使用的工具和發展該工具的研究者。

- that 子句真正的動詞是 provide，而不是 developed。developed 是來自原句 the clause relational analysis which was developed by... 的簡化形式。簡化的規則是關係子句中具有關係代名詞和 be 動詞後接現在或過去分詞時，關係代名詞和 be 動詞可以省略，因此此子句中關係代名詞 which 和 be 動詞 was 就可以刪除，只剩過去分詞的 developed。

- 最後提出本研究期望達到的三個目的，用對等連接詞 as well as 和 and 來連結。

範例1　句型

1.　　研究背景或主題　　, and there is a great deal of general literature on　　研究主題　　.

2. There is little specific guidance, however, on　　研究缺口　　.

3. Using　　研究對象　　 as an example, this paper will argue that　　分析工具或模式理論　　 developed by　　研究者　　 can provide a framework for　　研究目的 A　　, as well as giving　　研究目的 B　　, and a method of analyzing　　研究目的 C　　.

練習

請按照以上講解說明以及你自己的研究內容，填入以下段落的空格來撰寫摘要。

_____, and there is a great deal of general

literature on _____. There is little specific

guidance, however, on _____.

Using _____ as an example,

this paper will argue that _____

developed by _____ can provide a

framework for _____, as well as giving

_____, and a method of analyzing

_____.

範例 2

以下範例具備比較完整的元素，從一開始提出研究現況和主題，再寫研究的目的、材料、對象、分析方法、結果和義涵，幾乎涵括論文全文的重點。

① While the process of peer reviewing journal articles submitted for publication has been extensively investigated, the language of peer review is relatively unexplored. ② This paper studies evaluation in an electronic corpus of 228 reviews submitted to the journal *English for Specific Purposes (ESP)*. ③ The research focuses on the things or entities evaluated and the adjectives associated with these. ④ Entities and adjectives are categorized and quantified in order to ascertain what things are evaluated by reviewers and the qualities by which they are judged. ⑤ The findings suggest that reviewers take on multiple roles, at the same time discouraging the publication of work that fails to meet the required standards and offering encouragement to authors and guiding them towards publication. ⑥ These findings have implications for authors submitting research papers and journal editors.

儘管文獻已經廣泛探討過同儕審查期刊文稿的過程，但是對審查所使用文字的研究則相對缺乏。本文探討電子語料庫中 228 篇投稿 English for Specific Purposes (ESP) 期刊的審查意見。此研究聚焦在審查意見中的事項和相關的形容詞。這些事項和形容詞都被分類和量化，以確認審查者所審查的東西和評審的品質。研究的結果指出審查者扮演多重的角色，同時建議不刊登未符標準的論文、鼓勵作者並指導他們如何出版論文。這些發現對於投稿的作者和期刊的編輯都有很大啟發。

範例2 **講解**

1 While the process of peer reviewing journal articles submitted for publication has been extensively investigated, the language of peer review is relatively unexplored.

- 第 1 句寫研究現況和主題，等於是論文中的緒論。

- 句首的從屬連接詞 while 並不是指時間的「當…時候」，而是作「儘管；雖然」解。以 while 引導的從屬子句先指出目前有關期刊論文審查的研究很多，用現在完成式被動語態 has been investigated，表示這是一個從過去到現在一直都有人探討的領域。

- 第一個子句中的 submitted 並不是動詞，而是 peer reviewing journal articles which are submitted for... 的簡化，省略關係代名詞 which 和 be 動詞 are，只剩下過去分詞 submitted。

- 第二個子句則是提出本研究的主題，亦即對審查文字的研究並不多，所以值得探討。而時態使用現在式 is unexplored，是把時間點拉到現在，強調是一種普遍性現象。

2 This paper studies evaluation in an electronic corpus of 228 reviews submitted to the journal *English for Specific Purposes (ESP)*.

- 第 2 句寫本論文的目的以及使用的材料。

3 The research focuses on the things or entities evaluated and the adjectives associated with these.

- 第 3 句寫研究的焦點，也就是分析的對象。

4 Entities and adjectives <u>are categorized and quantified</u> in order to ascertain what things are evaluated by reviewers and the qualities <u>by which</u> they are judged.

- 第 4 句寫資料分析的方法，常用被動語態以強調客觀性和去個人化色彩，如句中的 are categorized and quantified。

- 句末出現 by which 加子句，此介系詞 by 原本應是放在子句最後如 which they are judged by，而 which 指的是其先行詞 the qualities，也就是 they are judged by the qualities 的意思。但因寫作時介系詞不宜放在句尾，因此通常就把 by 改置於關係代名詞 which 之前。

5 The <u>findings</u> <u>suggest</u> <u>that</u> reviewers take on multiple roles, at the same time discouraging the publication of work that fails to meet the required standards and offering encouragement to authors and guiding them towards publication.

- 第 5 句寫研究的結果，名詞 findings 可代換成 results。
- 動詞 suggest 也可用 indicate 取代。
- 連接詞 that 之後是接子句，說出研究的結果。

6 These findings have <u>implications</u> <u>for</u> authors submitting research papers and journal editors.

- 最後寫研究結果的義涵 (implications)，介系詞用 for，後接對什麼人或機構有所啟發或協助。

範例 2 句型

1. While ___研究領域___ has been extensively investigated, ___某研究主題___ is relatively unexplored.

2. This paper studies ___本研究的主題___.

3. The research focuses on ___本研究的重心或研究對象___.

4. ___本研究的資料___ are categorized and quantified in order to ascertain ___研究資料的效果或功能___.

5. The findings suggest that ___研究結果___.

6. These findings have implications for ___研究結果的義涵___.

練習

請按照以上講解說明以及你自己的研究內容，填入以下段落的空格來撰寫摘要。

While _____ has been extensively

investigated, _____ is relatively unexplored.

This paper studies _____.

The research focuses on _____.

_____ are categorized and quantified in order

to ascertain _____. The findings suggest that

_____. These findings have implications for

_____.

Introduction

　　論文的第一章緒論基本上是讓讀者了解這個研究的背景脈絡和理論基礎、其在整個研究領域的地位為何、此研究的主旨和特點又如何，以及作者為什麼要做這個研究、要回答哪些研究問題、研究結果的價值在哪裡等。這些資訊可以透過以下八個小節來具體呈現：

1. Research Background Information（研究背景）
2. Defining Concepts（定義概念）
3. Literature Review（文獻探討）
4. Research Gap（研究缺口）
5. Research Purpose（研究目的）
6. Research Questions（研究問題）
7. Research Value（研究價值）
8. Overview of the Paper（論文章節概述）

　　以上的緒論架構大體上呈現一種從普遍性（general）的內容如研究背景和領域，漸次寫至愈來愈特定（specific）的資訊如本研究的目的和價值等，使讀者對於整個研究內容的發展有較明確的預期，增進閱讀的效率。但並不是每篇論文都需要按照這樣的架構和順序來寫，而是依研究領域的寫作慣例（writing conventions）和作者個人的寫作風格（writing styles）而有或多或少的調整。

　　因緒論所包含的資訊內容較為複雜，每個小節在動詞時態的使用就比較不一致，我們通常只能把握一個原則，如果句子指涉的是普遍性和不受時間影響而變化的內容，例如經常性的事

實、標準化的流程或學界共同接受的準則等,就應該用現在式;
但若是指涉特定的內容和過去的事件,例如個別的事例、以前完
成的研究結果、不是普遍接受的理論等,就傾向用過去式。

　　以下再分述每個小節的段落寫作要點。

1

Research Background Information
研究背景

　　研究背景是要介紹本研究所處的領域 (field) 或大環境，通常會提到研究的一般性事實、趨勢或不同立場的觀點，藉以點出自己的研究定位，也等於為研究的主題先奠下脈絡或基礎，並說明自己的研究主題與廣泛研究領域之間的關係。

　　撰寫研究背景時一般會從概述性的陳述 (general statement) 描寫整個研究領域開始，往下行文則寫較特定的資訊 (specific information) 以進到研究主題。為支持某個立場或觀點，有時也會加入一些研究文獻的描述，但不像寫文獻探討那一節時那麼深入。

範例 1

　　以下範例是從研究的趨勢和兩種不同立場來寫研究背景，而且每種立場都各舉出學者的觀點作為支持，到最後作者也必須表明自己的立場，為整篇論文的立場定調。

---

① There has been an increasing interest in the relationship between translator training and market demands (see for example Li, 2003; Pym, 1993; Vienne, 1994). ② While all seem to agree that translation teaching cannot be entirely separate from market forces, opinions differ as to how translation training programs should relate to the real world of professional translation. ③ Some scholars have argued against simulated professional training in the school environment, holding that translation programs should be aimed at development of student translators' problem-solving abilities. ④ For instance, Mossop (1999) believes that it is unrealistic to expect translation graduates to arrive at the workplace and translate quickly and well. ⑤ Other researchers, however, advocate the inclusion of market needs into translation curriculum design, insisting that such training curricula will better prepare student translators for the translation work they are to undertake after graduation. ⑥ Ulrych, for instance, argues that "trainee translators need to be prepared for the conditions they will find in the working world" (1995: 253). ⑦ The present author also contends that authentic translation should be provided to students in order to reduce the "real world shock" for graduates at the workplace.

學界對於譯者訓練和市場需求關係的研究興趣愈來愈高（例如 Li, 2003; Pym, 1993; Vienne, 1994）。儘管所有人似乎都同意翻譯教學不能完全與市場脫鉤，但是對於翻譯訓練課程如何與專業翻譯的眞實世界結合卻有不同的意見。部分學者反對在學校環境中模擬翻譯職場，認為翻譯課程的目標應該是發展學生譯者解決問題的能力。例如 Mossop (1999) 認為，希望學生畢業後進入職場就能譯得又快又好是不切實際的事。然而，其他研究者則支持將市場需求整合至翻譯課程設計中，堅信如此的翻譯課程才能讓學生準備好在畢業後擔任翻譯工作。例如 Ulrych 主張：「受訓譯者需要爲職場上的情況做好準備。」(1995: 253) 而本文作者也認為應該提供學生實務翻譯工作，才能減少畢業生進入職場所受到的「現實衝擊」。

範例1 講解

1 There <u>has been</u> an <u>increasing</u> interest in the relationship between translator training and market demands (see <u>for example</u> Li, 2003; Pym, 1993; Vienne, 1994).

- 首句為概述性陳述，指出從過去以來愈來愈多人感到興趣的議題，時態用現在完成式 has been。
- 形容詞 increasing 也可代換成 growing 來搭配名詞 interest。
- 為了支持此句的陳述，作者引用相關文獻資料，並放在句尾的圓括號中，表示這些作者都研究過這個議題，這是一種資訊顯著引用方式 (information-prominent citation)，重點在於所引用的資訊，而研究者和出版資訊只是附加作為參考用。
- 圓括號中的 for example 也常寫成拉丁文的 e.g.，在其後可加逗號如 e.g., 或者不加逗號也可以。

2 <u>While</u> all seem to agree that translation teaching cannot be entirely separate from market forces, opinions differ as to how translation training programs should relate to the real world of professional translation.

- 承接上一句的研究議題，第 2 句寫研究者雖然有相同的看法，但也有不同的意見。
- 句首的從屬連接詞 while 表「儘管；雖然」，連接兩個句意對反的子句。

3

Some scholars <u>have argued</u> against simulated professional training in the school environment, <u>holding that</u> translation programs should be aimed at development of student translators' problem-solving abilities.

◉ 第 3 句開始寫比較特定的立場，時態使用現在完成式 have argued，呼應第 1 句的時態。

◉ 第一個子句先寫某些學者的立場，之後的分詞片語 holding that 所引導的子句再寫其意見。

4

<u>For instance</u>, Mossop (1999) believes <u>that</u> it is unrealistic to expect translation graduates to arrive at the workplace and translate quickly and well.

◉ 第 4 句承接第 3 句學者的立場再繼續提供更特定的資訊，也就是舉例子，因此句首的連接副詞用 for instance，也可代換成 for example。

◉ 之後就用作者顯著引用方式 (author-prominent citation)，讓作者的姓和出版年份作為句子主詞，that 之後再用子句陳述該研究者的意見。

5

<u>Other</u> researchers, <u>however,</u> advocate the inclusion of market needs into translation curriculum design, <u>insisting that</u> such training curricula will better prepare student translators for the translation work they are to undertake after graduation.

◉ 第 5 句開始轉換至另一群對立立場的研究，使用形容詞 other 就是要排除第 3 句所提到的 some scholars。

- 連接副詞 however 作爲一種轉折語，提示讀者句意在此作一反向的轉變。而把 however 放在主詞 researchers 和動詞 advocate 的中間，前後還有逗號，算是一種寫作上的變化。也可以把 however 置於句首，形成 However, other researchers advocate...。

- 此句句型類似第 3 句，第一個子句先寫其他研究者的立場，然後用分詞片語 insisting that 引導一個子句再寫其具體意見。

6   Ulrych, <u>for instance,</u> <u>argues that</u> "trainee translators need to be prepared for the conditions they will find in the working world" (1995: 253).

- 第 6 句則是和第 4 句的功能類似，承接第 5 句學者的立場，再接著提供更特定的例子。

- 連接副詞 for instance 置於主詞 Ulrych 和動詞 argues 中間，前後需加逗號。

- 而 argues that 之後是採直接引用 (direct quotation)，所引用的文字必須置於引號之內，而圓括號則放在引號和句號之間。

7   <u>The present author</u> also contends that authentic translation should be provided to students in order to reduce the "real world shock" for graduates at the workplace.

- 在介紹完兩種立場的研究者之後，作者在最後一句必須表明自己的立場。

- 句首作者直指自己爲 the present author，此種寫法類似中文寫作時自稱的「筆者」，以第三人稱自稱以表示客觀性；但近來愈來愈多的論文，尤其是質性研究和理工領域的文章常用第一人稱 I 或 we 來指稱研究者個人或團隊。

範例1 **句型**

1. There has been an increasing interest in ___研究議題___ (see for example ___引用文獻___).

2. While all seem to agree that ___所有研究者似乎都同意的看法___ , opinions differ as to ___研究者的不同意見___ .

3. Some scholars have argued against ___某些學者反對的立場___ , holding that ___這些學者的意見___ .

4. For instance, ___某學者 A___ believes that ___該學者的想法___ .

5. Other researchers, however, advocate ___其他研究者不同的立場___ , insisting that ___這些研究者的意見___ .

6. ___某學者 B___ , for instance, argues that ___該學者的主張___ .

7. The present author also contends that ___本文作者的立場與意見___ .

練習

請按照以上講解說明以及你自己的研究內容，填入以下段落的空格來撰寫研究背景。

There has been an increasing interest in _____

(see for example _____). While all seem to

agree that _____, opinions differ as to

_____. Some scholars have

argued against _____, holding that

_____. For instance,

_____ believes that

_____. Other researchers, however,

advocate _____, insisting that

_____. _____,

for instance, argues that _____. The present

author also contends that _____.

　　寫研究背景時也可能需要對照或比較兩個研究領域或主題，用以凸顯兩者之間的異同，並作爲本研究的理論基礎。以下範例是論文寫作中常採用的平行 (parallel) 結構，除第一句是概述外，之後的第 2、3 句與第 4、5 句都是相互平行對仗，除了讓全段讀起來較清楚，也讓讀者容易預期接下來要讀到的内容是什麼。基本架構由 5 個句子組成，以 A 與 B 的對照爲例，首句先說明 A 與 B 要作對照，接下來第 2 句和第 3 句介紹 A，而第 4 句和第 5 句就介紹 B。

① The forming of community in university courses in the U.S. probably ranges between two types of processes: a dialectic process and a rhetorical process. ② On the one hand, a dialectic process is a way of forming community that proceeds by question and answer and involves the participants in a process of refutation and mutual discovery. ③ This kind of community is most likely formed between specialists. ④ A rhetorical process, on the other hand, is a way of forming community that for one reason or another does not involve participants in a process of refutation. ⑤ This is more likely formed between students and instructors in lectures and seminars.

在美國大學課堂中形成社群**可能有兩種**過程：辯證過程**和**修辭過程。**在一方面**，辯證過程是以提問和回答以及反駁和探討**的方式**來形成社群。**此種社群最有可能是**由專家所形成。**另一方面**，修辭過程是以參與者不會提出反駁的**方式**形成。**這種可能**較有可能是由學生和教師在講課和專題研討中形成。

範例 2 講解

1 The forming of community in university courses in the U.S. probably <u>ranges</u> between two types of processes: a dialectic process and a rhetorical process.

- 首句先寫出是哪兩種領域或主題的對照,例如指出美國大學形成學術社群的兩種過程 (two types of processes) 為辯證過程和修辭過程 (a dialectic process and a rhetorical process)。
- 句中動詞使用 range 顯得簡潔生動,而且這是一普遍性的論述,因此用現在式。

2 <u>On the one hand,</u> a dialectic process is a way of forming community that proceeds by question and answer and involves the participants in a process of refutation and mutual discovery.

- 接下來分別介紹這兩種過程,先使用連接副詞 on the one hand 引介出第一種的辯證過程,讀者就會預期之後還會有 on the other hand 來引介第二種過程,這是論文寫作中常用的標記字 (signal word)。

3 This kind of community is most likely formed between specialists.

- 第 3 句是承接第 2 句的句意,繼續說明第一種的辯證過程。

4　A rhetorical process, <u>on the other hand,</u> is a way of forming community that for one reason or another does not involve participants in a process of refutation.

第 4 句果然出現連接副詞 on the other hand 來引介第二種的修辭過程，不過是插入在主詞 a rhetorical process 和動詞 is 之間，這樣的寫法顯得比較有變化。不然用 on the other hand 作為句首也可以，形成 On the other hand, a rhetorical process is a way of... 的句子。

5　This is more likely formed between students and instructors in lectures and seminars.

第 5 句是承接第 4 句的句意，繼續對第二種的修辭過程作說明。

範例 2 句型

1. ___研究主題___ probably ranges between two types of ___對照的主題___ :
   ___A___ and ___B___ .

2. On the one hand, ___A___ is a way of ___說明 A 的特性___ .

3. This kind of ___A___ is most likely ___承接上一句的句意，繼續說明 A 的特性___ .

4. ___B___ , on the other hand, is a way of ___說明 B 的特性___ .

5. This is more likely ___承接上一句的句意，繼續說明 B 的特性___ .

練習

請按照以上講解說明以及你自己的研究內容，填入以下段落的空格來表達兩個主題之間的對照。

_____ probably ranges between two types of

_____ : _____ and

_____ .

On the one hand, _____ is a way of

_____ . This kind of

_____ is most likely

_____ . _____ ,

on the other hand, is a way of _____ . This is

more likely _____ .

Defining Concepts

定義概念

大部分研究都會使用一些理論術語或抽象概念,而且不同學派立場的研究對同一個術語或概念很可能會有不同的定義和解釋,一旦讀者以自己的想法立場來解釋作者所使用的詞彙,就容易造成理解上的困擾,因此在撰寫緒論時就需要加以界定。

定義的方式可分為概念性定義 (conceptual definition) 和操作性定義 (operational definition)。如果是比較複雜的術語或概念系統,撰寫定義時可以單獨成節;但若是相對單純的名詞解釋,也可以寫在緒論的研究背景或者文獻探討中,不需要另外再寫一節。通常作者在探討文獻前就會寫好定義,讓讀者在閱讀文獻中的特定詞彙時不致產生不同的理解。總之,撰寫定義的位置很有彈性,但原則是在開展與此術語或概念相關的內容前都必須要先界定好其意義。

範例 1

下定義除了界定某一概念之外,還可提供相對的概念作為參照,以及進一步提供該概念的例子作為說明。以下範例中的幾個概念其實有不同的層次關係,從最上一層的 second language acquisition 開始,然後依序為 affective domain, personality variable/factor 到最下層的 self-esteem。行文的進展就是從第 1 句開始依序將這些概念介紹出來。

① Before I proceed with my discussion on second language acquisition, I need to define an important concept, the affective domain. ② This term has been useful in discussing the personality variables that we observe in second language learners. ③ The affective domain refers to the feelings that everyone experiences. ④ It is often contrasted with the cognitive domain, which deals with our analytical abilities. ⑤ An example of a personality factor that falls within the affective domain is the idea of self-esteem. ⑥ Your self-esteem has to do with your view of yourself. ⑦ In terms of second language acquisition, we often assume that high self-esteem leads to success in language acquisition.

在繼續往下探討第二語言習得之前，我需要先界定一個重要概念：情意領域。這個術語用於討論我們在第二語言學習者身上所觀察到的個性變項是很有用的。情意領域是指每個人都會體驗到的感受。它通常是與認知領域相對的概念，而認知領域是處理我們的分析能力。在情意領域中個性因素可以所謂的自尊為例，你的自尊就是你如何看待自己的觀點。在第二語言習得中，我們通常預設高度自尊會促使語言習得成功。

範例1 **講解**

1 Before I proceed with my discussion on second language acquisition, I need to define an important concept, the affective domain.

◉ 首句指出本文的研究主題是第二語言習得 (second language acquisition)，其中首先要定義的概念是情意領域 (affective domain)。

◉ 另可注意定義概念之前加逗號的寫法。

2 This term <u>has been</u> useful in discussing the personality variables that we observe in second language learners.

- 第 2 句描述為何需要定義這個概念，主要是因為據研究者觀察，它在本文所要討論的個性變項 (personality variable) 中是很有用的 (useful)。

- 動詞時態用現在完成式 has been，表示此概念從過去至今都很有用。

3 The affective domain <u>refers to</u> the feelings that everyone experiences.

- 第 3 句就直指情意領域的定義，動詞 refer to 是界定詞彙的常用片語，也可用 mean, deal with, be defined as, be concerned with, can be thought of as 等代換。

4 It is often contrasted with the cognitive domain, <u>which deals with</u> our analytical abilities.

- 第 4 句定義認知領域 (cognitive domain)，與所定義的情意領域作對照，用以凸顯兩者的差異。

- 句中 which 是關係代名詞，用以代替先行詞 cognitive domain，而 which 之前有逗號，表示它是非限定的用法；另外 which 之後的動詞 deal with 與 refer to 一樣，都是常用來撰寫定義的片語。

5 An example of a <u>personality factor</u> that falls within the affective domain is the idea of self-esteem.

◎ 第 5 句就界定的概念提供相關的例證，在所界定的情意領域中提出個性因素 (personality factor)，亦即自尊 (self-esteem) 的例子。

◎ 此句的 personality factor 與第 2 句中的 personality variable 是相同的意思，論文寫作中 variable 與 factor 可交替使用，以增加字彙使用的多樣性。

6   Your self-esteem <u>has to do with</u> your view of yourself.

◎ 第 6 句再針對自尊作簡短說明，句中動詞 have to do with 用來說明概念，也很接近下定義的用法，可以 involve, relate to, be considered to be 等代換。

7   In terms of second language acquisition, we often assume that high self-esteem leads to success in language acquisition.

◎ 最後一句又回到第 1 句提過的研究主題第二語言習得，有前後呼應的效果，並且把自尊的概念與語言習得成功聯結起來。

範例1 **句型**

為概念下定義的段落架構可由以下七個句子組成，但寫作時若不為所定義的概念作對比，則可省略第四句；若為求精簡，亦可省略第七句。

---

1. Before I proceed with my discussion on ___研究題目___, I need to define an important concept, ___所要定義的概念___.

---

2. This term has been useful in discussing ___所定義的概念要討論的主題___.

---

3. ___所定義的概念___ refers to ___所定義概念的內容___.

---

4. It is often contrasted with ___與所定義概念作對比的另一概念___, which deals with ___另一概念的定義內容___.（若不作概念的對比，則此句可省略）

---

5. An example of ___所討論的主題___ that falls within ___所定義的概念___ is the idea of ___所定義概念的例子___.

---

6. ___所定義概念的例子___ has to do with ___例子的內容___.

---

7. In terms of ___研究題目___, we often assume that ___研究者的假設___.（此句可省略）

練習

請按照以上講解說明以及你自己的研究內容，填入以下段落的空格來表達所要定義的概念。

Before I proceed with my discussion on _____,

I need to define an important concept, _____.

This term has been useful in discussing _____.

_____ refers to _____.

It is often contrasted with _____, which deals

with _____. An example of

_____ that falls within

_____ is the idea of

_____. _____

has to do with _____. In terms

of _____, we often assume that

_____.

範例 2

　　此範例著重如何區分並界定幾個性質相近、容易混淆的術語，爲了強調這些術語的緊密相關性，可以把它們寫在同一句，但要注意標點符號的使用方式。

① Before going any further, I would like to define some of the key educational terms I will be using in this paper. ② While the words are surely familiar to all teachers, there is considerable variability in the meanings attributed to them. ③ I will use assessment to refer to the process of gathering information about the quality of students' competence; evaluation I understand as the process of attributing meaning to the information gathered; testing is a scientific process of sampling performance with the goal of generalizing to competence; and marking is an attempt to sort performance along a scale (Azwell, 1992). ④ The importance of specifying these definitions, I hope, will quickly become apparent.

在往下進行之前，我想要先界定幾個在文中用到的重要教育詞彙。雖然所有的教師都很熟悉這些詞彙，但是大家對這些詞彙的理解仍有很大的歧異。我使用評量指涉取得學生資質資訊的過程；而評鑑就我理解是指賦予所蒐集資訊意義的過程；測驗是從學生表現中抽樣的科學過程，其目的是將學生的表現類推到他們的能力；而給分則是嘗試在同一量尺上測出學生的表現 (Azwell, 1992)。希望讀者在閱讀本文時，很快就能體會到界定這些詞彙的重要性。

範例2 講解

1 Before going any further, I would like to define some of the key educational terms I will be using in this paper.

○ 在進入文章的論述之前，通常會對文中重要概念下定義，例如本句 Before going any further, I would like to define... 就是常用的句型。另外之前範例 1 也有類似句型如 Before I proceed with my discussion on..., I need to define an important concept, ...。

2 While the words are surely familiar to all teachers, there is considerable variability in the meanings attributed to them.

○ 句首的 while 是常用的從屬連接詞，表「雖然」之意。而 while 還可代換為 although, though, even though, whereas 等，意義都一致。

3 I will use assessment to refer to the process of gathering information about the quality of students' competence; evaluation I understand as the process of attributing meaning to the information gathered; testing is a scientific process of sampling performance with the goal of generalizing to competence; and marking is an attempt to sort performance along a scale (Azwell, 1992).

○ 這句這麼長，顯然是全段的重心，雖然形式上是一個句子，但字數卻高達 59 個字。一般而言，這樣的句子過長，不宜多用。

◎ 但因作者要同時界定 4 個概念相近的詞彙，分別為 assessment, evaluation, testing, marking，為表現這些詞彙的關係緊密，可用分號代替句號。因此這個句子中出現 3 個分號，就等於是連結了 4 個句子，其句型公式為「句子 1；句子 2；句子 3；and 句子 4．」。另外要注意，句中的分號不可以用逗號代替。

◎ 而句尾 (Azwell, 1992) 則指出這些定義的文獻出處，是資訊顯著引用。

4 The importance of specifying these definitions, I hope, will quickly become apparent.

◎ 最後一句交待下文很快就會用到此處所界定的詞彙意義。

範例 2 句型

此為意義相近的數個概念（如 A, B, C, D）下定義的段落寫法。寫作重點是在第三句，該句可抵四個句子的份量，每句要用分號隔開，而非句號或逗號。

---

1. Before going any further, I would like to define some of the key ____研究領域____ terms I will be using in this paper.

---

2. While the words are surely familiar to all ____該領域的工作者____ , there is considerable variability in the meanings attributed to them.

---

3. I will use ____所定義的概念 A____ to refer to ____所定義概念 A 的內容____ ; ____所定義的概念 B____ I understand as ____所定義概念 B 的內容____ ; ____所定義的概念 C____ is ____所定義概念 C 的內容____ with the goal of ____所定義概念 C 的目標____ ; and ____所定義的概念 D____ is ____所定義概念 D 的內容____ .

---

4. The importance of specifying these definitions, I hope, will quickly become apparent.

練習

請按照以上講解說明以及你自己的研究內容，填入以下段落的空格來表達所要定義的概念。

Before going any further, I would like to define some of the key

_____ terms I will be using in this paper. While

the words are surely familiar to all _____,

there is considerable variability in the meanings attributed to

them. I will use _____ to refer to

_____; _____

I understand as _____;

_____ is _____

with the goal of _____; and

_____ is _____.

The importance of specifying these definitions, I hope, will quickly become

apparent.

範例 3

此段要定義 anxiety（焦慮），一開始先指出此概念在某研究領域的重要性，接下來引用學者對此概念的定義，之後再用自己的話把學者的定義用比較簡單的方式表達出來，這是比較簡短但結構清楚的段落。

① The construct of **anxiety** plays a major role in second language acquisition. ② Spielberger (1983:1) defined **anxiety** as "the subjective feeling of tension, apprehension, nervousness, and worry associated with an arousal of the automatic nervous system." ③ More simply put, **anxiety** is associated with feelings of uneasiness, frustration, self-doubt, apprehension, or worry.

焦慮**的構念在**第二語言習得**上扮演重要角色**。Spielberger (1983:1) **曾把焦慮界定為**「緊繃、憂慮、緊張和擔心，並引發自主神經系統的主觀感覺」。**簡單而言**，焦慮**與**不安、挫折、自我懷疑、憂慮或擔心的感覺**有關**。

範例 3 **講解**

1 The <u>construct</u> of **anxiety** <u>plays a major role in</u> second language acquisition.

- 首句先講要定義的概念在某研究領域的重要性，而 construct 是心理學上的概念，中文常譯為「構念」。

- 句型 ...play a major role in...（在…扮演重要角色）是常用片語，其中 major 可以代換為 important, essential, key, critical 等字；而 role 也可代換成 part，形成如 ...play an important/ essential part in... 等句型。

2 Spielberger (1983:1) <u>defined</u> anxiety as "the subjective feeling of tension, apprehension, nervousness, and worry associated with an arousal of the automatic nervous system."

- 第 2 句是下定義常用的句型，以引用學者的姓爲句子主詞，其後括號中顯示引用文獻出版年份、冒號再接頁數，屬作者顯著引用。

- 動詞 defined 用過去式主動語態，再接所定義的詞彙，而引述的定義內容則放在引號內。

- 本句也可用被動語態表示，如 Anxiety was definded as "..." by Spielberger (1983:1).。

3 <u>More simply put</u>, anxiety is associated with feelings of uneasiness, frustration, self-doubt, apprehension, or worry.

- 第 3 句是作者用自己的話來簡化學者所提供的定義。

- 句首用連接副詞 more simply put（簡單而言），也可以代換爲 to put it more simply, to put it briefly, to put the matter simply, simply stated, in simpler terms 等用法。

範例3 句型

1. The construct of ____所要定義的概念____ plays a major role in ___研究領域____.

2. ____引用學者的姓____ (____出版年份和引述的頁數____) defined ____所定義的概念____ as " ____定義的內容____ ."

3. More simply put, ____所定義的概念____ is associated with ___作者對定義的理解____.

練習

請按照以上講解說明以及你自己的研究內容，填入以下段落的空格來表達所要定義的概念。

The construct of _____ plays a major role in

_____. _____

(_____) defined

_____ as

"_____." More simply put,

_____ is associated with

_____.

範例 4

　　以下範例引用文獻中知名學者的重要定義，而且該定義還可分成不同的組成部分。至於本段定義內容的細節資訊則省略。

① Seminal work on defining **Communicative Competence (CC)** was carried out by **Michael Canale and Merrill Swain (1980)**, still the reference point for virtually all discussions of **CC** in relation to second language teaching. ② In **Canale and Swain's (1980)** definition, four different components made up the construct of **CC**. ③ The first two categories reflected the use of the linguistic system; the last two defined the functional aspects of communication. ...

界定溝通能力 (CC) 的重要研究是由 Michael Canale **和** Merrill Swain (1980) **所執行**，至今仍幾乎是第二語言教學上討論溝通能力**的參考基礎。在** Canale **和** Swain (1980) **的定義中，溝通能力此構念是由四個部分組成。**前兩個**範疇反映**語言系統的使用，後兩個**範疇則是界定**溝通的功能層面。……

範例 4 　講解

1　Seminal work on defining Communicative Competence (CC) was carried out by Michael Canale and Merrill Swain (1980), still the reference point for virtually all discussions of CC in relation to second language teaching.

　　○ 第 1 句中 seminal work 是很常用的搭配詞，指「重大有影響力的研究或作品」。其後接被動語態，形成「seminal work on + 研究主題 + was carried out by + 研究者」的句型。

◎ 爲了要強調此定義的重要性，逗號之後的名詞片語 still the reference point for... 可進一步說明此定義的重要地位。

◎ 所定義的概念第一次出現時須寫出全名（如 Communicative Competence）並於括號內寫出頭字詞 (acronym) 的簡稱（如 CC），第二次之後再提到這個詞彙時就只寫頭字詞 CC 即可。

2 In Canale and Swain's (1980) definition, four different components made up the construct of CC.

◎ 此句一開始寫兩位學者共同提出的定義，這時要用共同所有格，也就是只在第二位學者的名字後加 's。如果是兩位學者各自提出不同的定義，那就是分別所有格，須寫成 Canale's and Swain's definitions。

◎ 我們常用動詞片語 make up 表「組成」，例如此句是意指此定義的概念由四個部分 (components) 所組成，也就是由數個個體合組成一個整體，可代換爲 constitute。但若是倒過來表達一個整體是由數個個體所組成，就要用 consist of 或 comprise。如下句：

• The operating system consists of three components:
此操作系統由三個部分所組成：

3 The first two categories reflected the use of the linguistic system; the last two defined the functional aspects of communication.

◎ 第 3 句繼續說明定義組成的各個部分，可用 category 取代上句的 component。

◎ 此句由兩個子句組成，分別講兩個不同類型範疇的特性，中間用分號隔開。第二個子句的主詞省略 categories。

◎ 此句寫完後，作者就再針對四個不同範疇一一加以介紹，但在此省略其內容。

範例 4　句型

1. Seminal work on defining ＿＿所要定義的概念＿＿ was carried out by ＿＿研究者＿＿, still the reference point for virtually all discussions of ＿＿所定義的概念＿＿ in relation to ＿＿研究領域＿＿.

2. In ＿＿研究者姓名所有格＿＿ definition, ＿＿數量＿＿ different components made up the construct of ＿＿所定義的概念＿＿.

3. The ＿＿數量＿＿ categories reflected ＿＿所定義概念範疇的內容＿＿; the ＿＿數量＿＿ defined ＿＿所定義概念範疇的內容＿＿.

練習

請按照以上講解說明以及你自己的研究內容，填入以下段落的空格來引用學者的定義。

Seminal work on defining _____ was carried

out by _____, still the reference point for

virtually all discussions of _____ in relation to

_____. In _____

definition, _____ different components made

up the construct of _____.

The _____ categories reflected

_____; the _____

defined _____. ...

3

Literature Review
文獻探討

　　探討與自己研究相關的文獻可以顯示出你對該研究領域的熟悉程度，奠定本研究的理論基礎，並讓讀者了解研究主題的來龍去脈或已有研究結果的得失爭議。而最重要的是要找出自己的研究和同領域其他研究之間的關係。我們若把整個研究領域看作是一幅拼圖 (jigsaw puzzle)，則每個研究都是其中一小塊不同的圖。而文獻探討就是嘗試找出自己這塊圖的定位，與其他研究要如何拼湊在一起，使研究領域變得更完整，或甚至擴大原有的版圖。

　　探討文獻時可以依據研究主題的研究時間，從早期的研究開始探討至比較近期的研究；也可以按照其他研究和自己研究之間相關的程度，從關係比較疏遠探討至關係比較密切的研究。而探討的主題可以包括之前研究的理論、方法、工具、變項或結果等；探討的方式則可以使用彙整、分析、歸納、比較、乃至於批判不同文獻等論理過程。

　　在回顧文獻的過程中，不要忘了必須對引述的作者或研究作引用 (citation)，如果是以資訊爲主就把作者和出版年份置於圓括號內，稱爲資訊顯著引用 (information-prominent citation)；若是以作者爲主來支持自己的論述，就把作者的姓寫在文中，只把出版年份置於圓括號內，稱爲作者顯著引用 (author-prominent citation)。多作文獻引用可避免抄襲他人研究內容的疑慮。

範例 1

以下的範例是就認知型態此一概念作文獻回顧，如同大多數對某概念的探討一樣，長期以來一定會有不同的學者提出不同的看法，作者可列舉幾個代表性的觀點。

---

① Twenty years ago, educational theorists and researchers were investigating the concept of cognitive style: how the mind actually functions, how it processes information or is affected by each individual's perceptions. ② Various groups of researchers have worked with pieces of complex cognitive profile; each group has its own taxonomy and terminology. ③ For example, Witkin (1986) and Oltman et al. (1987) have written widely about field independent versus field dependent approaches. ④ Kagan and Messer (1985) have discussed reflectivity versus impulsivity in the responses of learners. ⑤ Hill (1981) has investigated cognitive style mapping. ⑥ Gregorc (1989) has done extensive work with his categories of learning, which serve as indicators of a learner's mediation abilities.

20 年前，教育理論家和研究者都在探討認知型態的概念：心智是如何運作、如何處理資訊或受個人知覺影響。不同研究者就複雜的認知特徵從事研究工作，各自提出分類和術語系統。例如 Witkin (1986) 和 Oltman 等人 (1987) 撰寫過很多場域獨立和場域依賴的方式。Kagan 和 Messer (1985) 討論過學習者反思和衝動的反應。Hill (1981) 探討過認知型態圖。Gregorc (1989) 則就其學習範疇做過廣泛研究，作為學習者調解能力的指標。

範例 1 **講解**

1 Twenty years ago, educational theorists and researchers <u>were investigating</u> the concept of cognitive style: how the mind actually functions, how it processes information or is affected by each individual's perceptions.

◎ 首句先交待文獻過去的背景和研究主題，時態用過去進行式 were investigating，強調是在過去某一時點，也就是 20 年前正在進行的事。

2 Various groups of researchers <u>have worked</u> with pieces of complex cognitive profile; each group has its own taxonomy and terminology.

◎ 第 2 句承接上句的句意，繼續描述研究者的工作。

◎ 動詞時態使用現在完成式 have worked，顯示這些研究從過去到現在都一直還有研究者在做。

◎ 此句有兩個子句，中間用分號隔開。

3 <u>For example</u>, Witkin (1986) and Oltman, <u>et al.</u> (1987) <u>have written</u> widely about field independent versus field dependent approaches.

◎ 前兩句都是一般性的背景陳述，第 3 句開始寫較為具體個別的研究文獻。

◎ 句首用連接副詞 for example，承接上句所說的研究者工作，舉出特定的例子。

69

- 此句的例子引用兩個研究，第二個研究的作者之後出現拉丁文 et al.，意指英文的 and others，也就是說還有其他的研究者未寫出來。

- 動詞時態使用現在完成式 have written，表示作者認爲這些研究雖然已經結束，但其研究結果從過去到現在一直都還有影響力。

4 Kagan and Messer (1985) <u>have discussed</u> reflectivity versus impulsivity in the responses of learners.

- 第 4 句也是引述個別的文獻，動詞時態使用現在完成式 have discussed。

- 注意 discuss 是及物動詞，後面直接加受詞，但台灣同學有時會加介系詞寫成 *discuss about，這是錯誤的用法。

5 Hill (1981) <u>has investigated</u> cognitive style mapping.

- 第 5 句繼續引述個別研究，動詞時態一樣使用現在完成式 has investigated。

6 Gregorc (1989) <u>has done</u> extensive work with his categories of learning, <u>which</u> serve as indicators of a learner's mediation abilities.

- 最後仍是引述個別研究，動詞時態使用現在完成式 has done。

- 句中關係代名詞 which 之前有逗號，表示這是非限定用法，只是對先行詞 categories of learning 加以補充說明。

範例 1 句型

1. ___數字___ years ago, ___某研究領域___ theorists and researchers were investigating the concept of ___研究所探討的概念___ .

2. Various groups of researchers have worked with ___研究者的工作___ .

3. For example, ___研究者___ (___出版年份___) have written widely about ___研究者所撰寫的主題___ .

4. ___研究者___ (___出版年份___) have discussed ___研究者所討論的主題___ .

5. ___研究者___ (___出版年份___) has investigated ___研究者所探究的主題___ .

6. ___研究者___ (___出版年份___) has done extensive work with ___研究者工作的主題___ .

練習

請按照以上講解說明以及你自己的研究內容，填入以下段落的空格來撰寫文獻探討。

_____ years ago,

_____ theorists and researchers were

investigating the concept of _____. Various

groups of researchers have worked with _____.

For example, _____

(_____) have written widely about

_____. _____

(_____) have discussed

_____. _____

(_____) has investigated

_____. _____

(_____) has done extensive work with

_____.

範例 2

　　以下範例的不同研究文獻具有相同的立場，也就是都同意電腦輔助溝通 (CMC) 在第二語言學習上的益處，但是這種益處有不同面向，需要回顧各種研究來加以印證。

① Recent **CALL** research has suggested that **CMC** may indeed facilitate processes beneficial to second-language learning. ② These specific benefits include increased participation among students (Beauvois, 1992; Kern, 1995; Warschauer, 1996), an increased quantity of learner output (Chun, 1994; Kelm, 1992), and an increased quality of learner output (Beauvois, 1998; Chun, 1994; Kern, 1995). ③ Students may also view **CMC** as less threatening, which can result in their increased willingness to try out new hypotheses (Kelm, 1996; Warschauer, 1996). ④ A higher quality of learner output also has been reported. ⑤ Kern (1995) found that students were linguistically more creative during CMC.

近來電腦輔助語言學習 (CALL) 的研究指出，電腦輔助溝通 (CMC) **可能有助於**第二語言學習。**具體益處包括增進**學生參與 (Beauvois, 1992; Kern, 1995; Warschauer, 1996)，**促進**學習者產出**的數量** (Chun, 1994; Kelm, 1992) 和學習者產出**的品質** (Beauvois, 1998; Chun, 1994; Kern, 1995)。學生**也視**電腦輔助溝通較不具威脅感，**可提高**嘗試語言假設的意願 (Kelm, 1996; Warschauer, 1996)。**也有報告指出**學習者產出的品質提升。Kern (1995) **發現**學生在使用電腦輔助溝通時，語言表現更有創意。

範例2 講解

1　Recent CALL research <u>has suggested</u> that CMC may indeed facilitate processes beneficial to second-language learning.

⊙ 第1句先交待近來研究領域 (CALL) 中某一研究主題 (CMC) 的研究結果，傾向有利於第二語言學習，是一種較爲普遍性的論述。

⊙ 因爲是描述從過去到現在的一股研究趨勢，因此時態用現在完成式 has suggested。

2　These specific benefits <u>include</u> <u>increased</u> participation among students (Beauvois, 1992; Kern, 1995; Warschauer, 1996), an <u>increased</u> quantity of learner output (Chun, 1994; Kelm, 1992), and an <u>increased</u> quality of learner output (Beauvois, 1998; Chun, 1994; Kern, 1995).

⊙ 第2句承接上句的普遍性論述之後，開始介紹較爲特定具體的研究文獻以延伸第1句提到對學習第二語言的助益，總共分爲三類，各自引用兩到三組的研究文獻。

⊙ 在動詞 include 之後的三組研究文獻寫法是平行結構，都是「形容詞 increased + 名詞片語 + （引用文獻）」。

⊙ 因爲寫作重點是資訊內容，因此三組文獻的引用如研究者的姓和出版年份都寫在圓括號內，當作補充資料，是種資訊顯著引用。

3 Students may also view CMC as less threatening, which can result in their increased willingness to try out new hypotheses (Kelm, 1996; Warschauer, 1996).

◎ 第 3 句是從研究對象學生的觀點，來印證第 1 句和第 2 句所提 CMC 的好處，而且和第 2 句一樣是使用資訊顯著的引用方式。

◎ 句中片語 result in 表「造成；導致」，跟另一片語 result from 表「由於」的因果關係相反。

4 A higher quality of learner output also has been reported.

◎ 第 4 句也是接續前面的語意，換個方式來寫使用 CMC 的益處，句型則用現在完成式被動語態 has been reported，是強調從過去到現在一直都有效的研究結果。

5 Kern (1995) found that students were linguistically more creative during CMC.

◎ 第 5 句是針對第 4 句的研究結果提出具體個別的研究文獻來支持，此句是以研究者的姓作為句子主詞，其後圓括號是出版年份，這是作者顯著引用，用意在借重研究者的權威來支持此論述。

◎ 此時的動詞時態轉變成過去式 found，主要是因為個別的研究在過去某時間點已經結束，與第 4 句強調一般性研究趨勢時用現在完成式的時間點要求不同。

範例 2　**句型**

1. Recent _____研究領域_____ research has suggested that _____研究主題_____ may indeed facilitate processes beneficial to _____有益處的事項_____ .

2. These specific benefits include increased _____有益處的事項_____ (___引用文獻___), an increased quantity of _____有益處的事項_____ (___引用文獻___), and an increased quality of _____有益處的事項_____ (___引用文獻___).

3. _____研究對象_____ may also view _____研究主題_____ as _____有益處的事項_____ , which can result in _____有益處事項造成的結果_____ (___引用文獻___).

4. _____有益處的事項_____ also has been reported.

5. _____研究者_____ (___出版年份___) found that _____有益處的事項_____ .

練習

請按照以上講解說明以及你自己的研究內容，填入以下段落的空格來撰寫文獻探討。

Recent _____ research has suggested

that _____ may indeed facilitate processes

beneficial to _____. These specific benefits

include increased _____

(_____), an increased quantity of

_____ (_____),

and an increased quality of _____

(_____). _____

may also view _____ as

_____, which can result in

_____ (_____).

_____ also has been reported.

_____ (_____)

found that _____.

Research Gap
研究缺口

　　寫完文獻探討後，接著要指出文獻中目前研究不足之處或缺口，之後才能引介出自己研究的必要性。建立研究缺口，也就是明確指出該研究領域還有哪些不足或尚未研究的地方？哪些問題尚未解決或不夠完善？或是需要進一步延伸擴展之前的研究結果等。這些缺口可以由作者目前的研究來加以補足或深化。這節行文通常很短，兩三句即已足夠，也可以和接下來的研究目的和研究價值合併寫成一段。

範例 1

　　本段只有兩句，但兩句間具有「因果關係」。第 1 句先寫研究缺口，第 2 句寫為彌補缺口，所需要從事另一新議題的研究。

---

① As shown in the above literature review, existing research in interpretation anxiety has ignored the role of L2 anxiety in interpreters. ② Hence, in order to help fill this gap in our knowledge, this study investigated the probable existence of foreign language anxiety in student interpreters.

如同以上文獻探討所言，現存針對口譯焦慮的研究都忽略口譯者第二語言 (L2) 焦慮的角色。因此，為填補我們對此了解的不足，本研究調查口譯學生所可能具有的外語焦慮。

範例 1 講解

1 <u>As shown</u> in the above literature review, existing research in interpretation anxiety has ignored the role of L2 anxiety in interpreters.

- ◎ 第 1 句承接文獻探討的結果，指出現存研究中的缺口。
- ◎ 句首的 as shown 也可以代換成 as indicated, as mentioned, as noted, as discussed 等，但不能寫成 *as it was mentioned。

2 <u>Hence</u>, in order to help <u>fill this gap</u> in our knowledge, this study investigated the probable existence of foreign language anxiety in student interpreters.

- ◎ 句首以連接副詞 hence 表達「因果關係」，「因」是研究缺口，「果」則是爲彌補缺口所從事的研究。其他常用表達「因果關係」的連接副詞還有 therefore, thus, as a result, in consequence, for this reason 等。
- ◎ 句中片語 fill this gap 可代換成 bridge this gap，是陳述研究缺口常用的片語。

範例 1 句型

1. As shown in the above literature review, existing research in ___研究領域___ has ignored the role of ___被忽略的角色___.

2. Hence, in order to help fill this gap in our knowledge, this study investigated the probable existence of ___本研究所要探討的議題___.

練習

請按照以上講解說明以及你自己的研究內容，填入以下段落的空格來表達
研究缺口。

As shown in the above literature review, existing research

in _____ has ignored the role of

_____. Hence, in order to help fill this gap

in our knowledge, this study investigated the probable existence of

_____.

範例 2

　　此範例全段五句中，前三句是針對過去研究不足之處作鋪陳，最後兩句才指出研究缺口，邏輯語意關係的銜接很緊密。

---

① Most of the previous studies on **OOP** (object-oriented programming) described **a single investigator** who gave a course on the topic, and determined the contents of the course and the order of their presentation. ② The studies reported the problems that arose while teaching the course, and suggestions for improvements. ③ Other studies were based on **a single questionnaire**, which aimed to examine specific concepts. ④ **We did not find any publications** that reported a long and formal research project on teaching OOP. ⑤ There was a **noticeable absence** of research projects dealing with **young novices** such as high school students.

過去針對物件導向程式設計 (OOP) 的研究大多數都是在描述某一研究者所開設的課程及其課程的內容和教學程序。**這些研究報告了教學期間所發生的問題與改進的建議。**其他研究則是以某份問卷調查**為基礎，旨在檢視**某些特定概念。我們**並未找到任何刊物可提供** OOP 教學的**長期研究正式報告。**在探討如高中生這種年輕新使用者**的研究是完全闕如。**

範例 2 講解

1   Most of the previous studies on **OOP** (object-oriented programming) described a single investigator who gave a course on the topic, and determined the contents of the course and the order of their presentation.

- ◎ 第 1 句先陳述該研究主題 (OOP) 在之前大部分的研究中是如何進行的。
- ◎ 句首表「大多數」時可以用「most of the + 名詞」如 most of the previous studies，或者也可以用「most + 名詞」如 most previous studies。但台灣同學常寫成「most the + 名詞」如 *most the previous studies，這是錯誤用法。另外，如果 most of 之後接的是代名詞「most of + 代名詞」如 most of those studies/his studies，就不能省略 of 寫成 *most those studies/his studies。
- ◎ 動詞用過去式的 described，強調是過去所從事的研究。

2   The studies reported the problems that arose while teaching the course, and suggestions for improvements.

- ◎ 此句承接第 1 句的語意，繼續說明過去研究方法的結果和貢獻。
- ◎ 句中動詞 arose 是 arise 的過去式，它是不及物動詞，其原意是「上升」，但和 problem 或 difficulty 搭配，意思就變成「產生困難」。如以下例句：
  - Unexpected problems/difficulties arose in the course of their research.
    他們的研究過程中產生無法預期的困難。

3   Other studies were based on a single questionnaire, which aimed to examine specific concepts.

◎ 第 3 句也是說明過去的研究，但因爲所使用的研究方法與第 1 句不同，因此句首用 other studies 來和第 1 句的 most of the previous studies 作區隔。

4   We did not find any publications that reported a long and formal research project on teaching OOP.

◎ 這句開始明確指出過去研究文獻的缺口，第一個就是缺乏對該研究主題的長期和正式的研究報告 (a long and formal research project)。

5   There was a noticeable absence of research projects dealing with young novices such as high school students.

◎ 最後一句也是撰寫研究缺口，指出該領域缺乏針對某特定對象 (young novices such as high school students) 的研究。

◎ 句中名詞 absence 原意是「缺席」，而片語 absence of research projects 意指「缺乏研究」。也可以用 lack 來取代 absence。

範例 2 **句型**

1. Most of the previous studies on ___研究主題___ described ___之前研究使用的方法___.

2. The studies reported the problems that arose while ___研究過程___, and suggestions for improvements.

3. Other studies were based on ___其他研究使用的方法___, which aimed to examine ___所要達成的目標___.

4. We did not find any publications that reported a long and formal research project on ___研究主題___.

5. There was a noticeable absence of research projects dealing with ___研究缺口___.

練習

請按照以上講解說明以及你自己的研究內容，填入以下段落的空格來撰寫研究缺口。

Most of the previous studies on _____

described _____. The studies reported the

problems that arose while _____,

and suggestions for improvements. Other studies were

based on _____, which aimed to

examine _____. We did not find any

publications that reported a long and formal research project on

_____. There was a noticeable absence of

research projects dealing with _____.

Research Purpose
研究目的

　　研究缺口寫完通常就接著寫研究目的，藉以凸顯研究目的就是爲了補足研究領域的缺口，這樣才是合理的邏輯發展，也才能說服讀者這是一個有新意而值得研究的主題。

範例 1

　　此範例一開頭就直指研究的目的和研究方法，先寫一般性的研究目的 (purpose)，接下來再分寫兩個較具體特定要執行的目標 (aim)，如此寫作較具有層次感。

---

① The purpose of the study reported here was to explore teachers' beliefs about their roles as ESL teachers through an analysis of metaphors they produced. ② The specific aims in this report are (a) to identify the metaphors that ESL teachers use to characterize their roles and (b) to elucidate some of the theoretical assumptions about teaching and learning ESL reflected in those metaphors.

本研究的目的在透過分析教師提出的隱喻，**來探究**他們對於擔任以英語爲第二語言 (ESL) 老師角色的信念。**此報告具體的目標為：(a) 指出** ESL 老師用來形容其角色的隱喻，**以及 (b) 闡明**在這些隱喻中所反映**有關** ESL **教學的理論預設**。

範例1 講解

1 | The <u>purpose</u> of the study reported here was <u>to explore</u> teachers' beliefs about their roles as ESL teachers <u>through</u> an analysis of **metaphors they produced.**

◎ 句首的 purpose 也可代換成 goal, objective 等字,而不定詞 to explore 也可用 to investigate, to examine 等取代。

◎ 介系詞 through 有「透過;憑藉」之意,也就是透過文中分析隱喻的方式來達到原先設定的研究目的。

2 | The specific <u>aims</u> in this report are (a) <u>to identify</u> the metaphors that ESL teachers use to characterize their roles <u>and</u> (b) <u>to elucidate</u> some of the theoretical assumptions about **teaching and learning ESL reflected in those metaphors.**

◎ 第 2 句用的 aim 也是「目標,目的」,通常比 purpose 來得具體特定一些。

◎ 兩個具體的目標分別寫成 (a) 和 (b) 兩個不定詞 to identify... 和 to elucidate... 的平行結構,用對等連接詞 and 連接,比較清楚易懂。

1. The purpose of the study reported here was to explore ___研究主題___
through an analysis of ___研究對象所產出的資料___.

2. The specific aims in this report are (a) to identify ___具體的研究目標
A___ and (b) to elucidate some of the theoretical assumptions about
___具體的研究目標 B___.

練習

請按照以上講解說明以及你自己的研究內容，填入以下段落的空格來撰寫研究目的。

The purpose of the study reported here was to explore

_____ through an analysis of

_____. The specific aims in this report are (a)

to identify _____ and (b) to elucidate some of

the theoretical assumptions about _____.

範例 2

此範例與上述範例 1 先寫研究目的的方式不同，此段一開始先寫研究的背景和之前類似文獻，再提出研究缺口或利基 (niche)，到最後才寫出兩個研究目的，包括作者還要以目前研究與之前另一研究結果相比較。

① To ensure that translation programs best meet the constantly changing social needs and the needs of students, assessment must be carried out to ascertain the real needs of both students and professional translators. ② A study of the needs of professional translators in Hong Kong conducted earlier in 1999 by the present researcher discovered noticeable differences between what translation programs offered and what professional translators required at work, and provided useful suggestions for curriculum innovation (Li, 2000). ③ However, the needs of translation students, who are tomorrow's professionals, have not been studied yet in the English vs. Chinese translation context. ④ It is therefore the intent of the present study to examine translation students' needs, followed by a comparison with the findings of my earlier study on professional translators.

為確保翻譯課程能符合經常變動的社會需求以及學生需求，必須執行評量以確定學生和專業譯者的真正需求。之前在 1999 年，本文作者做過香港專業譯者的需求研究，發現翻譯課程所教授與專業譯者在職場所需有明顯差異，並提出課程改革的有效建議 (Li, 2000)。然而，身為未來專業譯者的翻譯學生，其在中英翻譯情境的需求卻從未被探討過。因此，本研究目的在於檢視翻譯學生的需求，所得結果再與我之前針對專業譯者所做的研究結果相互比較。

範例2 **講解**

1 To ensure that translation programs best meet the
constantly changing social needs and the needs of students,
assessment must be carried out to ascertain the real needs
of both students and professional translators.

- 第 1 句陳述此研究的背景和屬性，點出需求分析的重要性。
- 因爲是普遍性的陳述，時態用現在式。
- 句中兩個不定詞 to ensure 和 to ascertain 是同義詞，都是指 to
  make certain（確定）。

2 A study of the needs of professional translators in Hong
Kong conducted earlier in 1999 by the present researcher
discovered noticeable differences between what translation
programs offered and what professional translators required
at work, and provided useful suggestions for curriculum
innovation (Li, 2000).

- 第 2 句簡述作者以前所做過的類似研究，並報告其研究結果，也
  是爲目前的研究提供背景和參照。
- 因爲是描述過去所做的研究，時態轉爲過去式。最後並加上引
  用之前研究的資訊 (Li, 2000)。
- 句中提到的 the present researcher 指的是此研究的研究者，也
  可以寫成 the author of this paper（本文作者）。

3 However, the needs of translation students, who are tomorrow's professionals, have not been studied yet in the English vs. Chinese translation context.

- 第 3 句用連接副詞 however 開頭，顯示與前句的對反關係，也就是目前研究領域的缺口或是本研究的利基，形成值得做此研究的理由。

- 句中的關係代名詞 who 之前有逗號，表示是非限定用法。形容詞子句 who are tomorrow's professionals 只是用來補充說明先行詞 translation students，即使整個子句省略，也不會影響句意的完整。

- 句中出現的拉丁文 vs. 是 versus（相對立）的簡寫，這是一個字，因此只能用一個句點簡寫成 vs. 或 v.；但很多人會把兩個字母各加一個句點誤寫成 *v.s.。

4 It is therefore the intent of the present study to examine translation students' needs, followed by a comparison with the findings of my earlier study on professional translators.

- 第 4 句才明確指出本研究的目的，連接副詞 therefore 放到 be 動詞之後，也可以放在句首再加逗號，形成 Therefore, it is the intent of the present study to...。

- 此句用 intent 表「目的」，而因為這一句中要寫兩個研究目的，作者就用不定詞 to examine 帶出第一個目的，而用過去分詞片語 followed by 引介出第二個目的。

1. To ensure that ___研究背景的議題___ best meet ___研究主題___ needs and the needs of ___研究主題___, ___此次要做的研究___ must be carried out to ascertain the real needs of ___研究主題___.

2. A study of the needs of ___之前研究主題___ conducted earlier in ___執行研究的年份___ by the present researcher discovered ___之前研究的結果___, and provided useful suggestions for ___之前研究結果的應用___ (___引用之前研究文獻___).

3. However, the needs of ___目前研究主題___ have not been studied yet in ___之前研究主題的領域或情境___.

4. It is therefore the intent of the present study to examine ___研究主題___, followed by a comparison with the findings of ___其他研究___.

練習

請按照以上講解說明以及你自己的研究內容，填入以下段落的空格來撰寫
研究目的。

To ensure that _____ best meet

_____ needs and the needs of

_____, _____

must be carried out to ascertain the real needs of

_____. A study of the needs of

_____ conducted earlier in

_____ by the present researcher discovered

_____, and provided useful suggestions for

_____ (_____).

However, the needs of _____ have not been

studied yet in _____. It is therefore the intent of

the present study to examine _____, followed

by a comparison with the findings of _____.

Research Questions
研究問題

　　研究問題是把上述的研究目的用問句的型式加以操作化。研究目的通常是一種普遍性的論述，但若要落實這些論述還需要較為具體特定的步驟或行為，可以藉由幾個研究問題的方式呈現。整個研究的執行就是為了回答這些研究問題，而一旦回答了這些問題，也就等於達到了研究目的。

　　有些作者寫了研究目的，就不一定會寫研究問題，Weissberg 和 Buker (1990) 認為研究目的寫得好，讀者就可以從研究目的的內容推論 (infer) 出研究問題。但筆者覺得為提高論文的可讀性 (readability)，就算研究問題的內容資訊與研究目的多少有些重複，可是明確寫出研究問題可以讓讀者更清楚此研究要處理的重點是什麼。而且寫到論文後面的討論一章時，還可以用研究問題作為小節的標題一一回答，達到論文前後呼應的效果，結構上也比較工整。

　　至於研究問題的寫法，如果問題較多且長，可以條列的方式逐項呈現；如果問題的文字不多，就可寫在同一個段落中。而研究問題又可分為開放性 (open-ended questions) 和封閉性問題 (closed questions) 兩種型式。開放性問題常以 what, how, why 等疑問詞作為句首，其回答的內容通常較為豐富開放，較適用於質性研究。封閉性問題是以 be 動詞或助動詞作為句首，又稱為 yes-no question，因為回答時通常以 yes 或 no 開頭。這種問題較適用於量性實驗研究上，例如做完實驗得到結果後只要回答是否接受實驗假設。

範例 1

　　以下範例為條列式問題的寫法，而作者提出的兩個研究問題分別為開放性和封閉性問題。

---

① To address the issues already outlined and to begin to fill the gaps in the previous research, the present study was designed to address the following research questions:

② (1) What characteristics of teacher commentary appear to influence student revision?

③ (2) Do revisions influenced by teacher feedback lead to substantive and effective changes in students' papers?

為探討稍早提出的議題並開始填補以前研究的空缺，我們設計此研究以回答下列問題：

(1) 老師的評語具有**什麼**特性似可影響學生的修訂過程？

(2) 受老師回饋影響的修訂**是否能**有效實質地改進學生論文？

範例1 **講解**

1　To <u>address</u> the <u>issues</u> already outlined and to begin to fill the gaps in the previous research, the present study was designed to <u>address</u> the following research <u>questions</u>:

◉ 這個句子幾乎可以套用在大部分論文的研究問題寫作。

◉ 動詞 address 的意思跟「地址」無關，而是指「處理；應付」，其後可以搭配名詞如 issues 和 questions 等。

2   (1) <u>What</u> characteristics of teacher commentary appear to influence student revision?

◉ 第一個問題是開放性問題，用疑問詞 what 作句首。

3   (2) <u>Do</u> revisions influenced by teacher feedback lead to substantive and effective changes in students' papers?

◉ 第二個問題是封閉性問題，用助動詞 do 作句首。

範例 1　句型

1. To address the issues already outlined and to begin to fill the gaps in the previous research, the present study was designed to address the following research questions:

2. (1) What _____第一個研究問題_____ ?

3. (2) Do _____第二個研究問題_____ ?

練習

請按照以上講解說明以及你自己的研究內容，填入以下段落的空格來撰寫研究問題。

To address the issues already outlined and to begin to fill the gaps in

the previous research, the present study was designed to address the

following research questions:

(1) What _____?

(2) Do _____?

範例 2

　　以下範例是將研究目的和三個研究問題寫在同一段而不分項，但仍以研究問題為重心。作者一開始先寫出研究目的是什麼，接著表明本研究是要回答哪三個問題。

① The purpose of this paper is to report on an investigation of one particular subset of learners' beliefs, i.e. what learners think about how best to approach the task of learning a second language. ② Answers were sought to the following questions: ③ Do language learners hold such beliefs? ④ Are the beliefs reflected in what learners say they do to learn a second language? ⑤ And finally, what is the significance of such beliefs?

本論文的目的是報告某特定學習者信念**的調查，也就是**學習者認為學習第二語言最好的方式為何。**本研究旨在回答以下問題**：語言學習者**是否**具備這些信念？這些信念**是否**反映在學習者所說學習第二語言的行為上？**以及最後一個問題**，這些信念的意義**是什麼**？

範例 2　講解

1　The purpose of this paper is to report on <u>an investigation of</u> one particular subset of learners' beliefs, <u>i.e.</u> what learners think about how best to approach the task of learning a second language.

　◎ 首句寫研究目的，以 an investigation of 帶出研究的主題 one particular subset of learners' beliefs。但這樣的主題較為籠統，需要進一步說明。

○ 作者用拉丁文的縮寫 i.e.，等於英文的 that is（也就是說），來
帶出比較具體的研究問題。

2 Answers <u>were sought</u> to the following questions:

○ 此句用來引介出個別的研究問題，可以直接借用至論文寫作中，
類似句型還有：

- In our study we sought to answer the following questions:
  我們的研究尋求回答以下的問題：

- This paper seeks to address the following questions:
  本文尋求探討以下問題：

- The present study attempted to investigate the following
  questions:
  本研究嘗試調查以下問題：

○ 本句中 sought 是 seek 的過去分詞，前面加 were 形成被動語
態。

3 <u>Do</u> language learners hold such beliefs?

○ 從第 3 句開始撰寫更具體個別的研究問題。

○ 此句以助動詞 do 為句首，是一種封閉性問題。

4 <u>Are</u> the beliefs reflected in what learners say they do to
learn a second language?

○ 第 4 句用 be 動詞 are 作為句首，也是封閉性問題。

5 And <u>finally</u>, <u>what</u> is the significance of such beliefs?

◯ 最後一句用對等連接詞 and 作句首，再加連接副詞 finally 來表達次序上的最後一個問題，但其實省略 and 也可以。

◯ 其後的問句用 what 開頭，是開放性問題。

範例 2

1. The purpose of this paper is to report on an investigation of ___研究主題___ , i.e. ___從研究主題出發的研究問題___ .

2. Answers were sought to the following questions:

3. Do ___第一個研究問題___ ?

4. Are ___第二個研究問題___ ?

5. And finally, what ___第三個研究問題___ ?

練習

請按照以上講解說明以及你自己的研究內容，填入以下段落的空格來撰寫
研究目的和研究問題。

The purpose of this paper is to report on an investigation of

_____ , i.e._____ .

Answers were sought to the following questions: Do

_____ ? Are _____ ?

And finally, what _____ ?

Research Value
研究價值

Introduction

　　研究價值通常可從研究的實用效益性 (practical benefits) 和理論重要性 (theoretical importance) 兩個層面來撰寫，盡量透顯該研究的貢獻。所謂實用效益性指的是研究結果可以解決某個實務問題或提升流程效率等；而理論重要性則是指研究發現可以解釋某個現象或提出某種普遍適用的模型等。但研究者對自己研究價值的陳述不能流於誇大自滿。基本上，就算作者對於自己研究成果很有信心，也都不願做出百分之百肯定的主張，因此用字會較為保守謹慎，尤其會使用相當多的助動詞如 may, might, should, could 等，以減緩或降低論述的強度 (reduce the strength of a statement)，也就是所謂的「避險」(hedging)。

範例 1

　　以下範例中的研究提出實用和理論上的價值，同時也使用幾項「避險」的文字機制。

---

① This is done with the hope that it may provide an alternative solution to the problem of manually demonstrating theories in an educational environment. ② Additionally, the system may serve as a basis for the study of automatic measurement systems in an instrumentation course. ③ The simplicity of operation should enable the student to observe details required in all systems without the usual problem of having to learn complex operating procedures.

做這個研究是**希望能對**在教育環境中使用人工方式展示理**論的**問題，提供另一種解決方案。除此之外，此系統**可作為**探討儀器課程中自動測量系統**之基礎**。其操作的便易性**應可使**學生仔細觀察所有系統，避免學習複雜操作程序所帶來的問題。

範例1 **講解**

1 This is done with the <u>hope</u> that it <u>may provide an alternative solution to the problem of</u> manually demonstrating theories in an educational environment.

◎ 寫研究價值要「避險」時常會用到 hope 這個字，畢竟研究有何貢獻是研究者主觀的期待，是否真能達到原先預期的價值很難確知，所以用 hope 來表示謙遜並降低宣稱的強度，也可用「It is hoped + that 子句」的結構。

◎ 而 that 之後的子句中使用助動詞 may 也是表達作者的主觀期望和不是百分之百確定的主張。

◎ 另外，**provide an alternative solution to the problem of** 是用來陳述解決某一問題的句型，算是一種實用效益性的研究價值。

2 <u>Additionally</u>, the system <u>may serve as a basis for the study of</u> automatic measurement systems in an instrumentation course.

◎ 句首連接副詞 additionally 用以表達本研究還有第二個研究價值，可代換成 in addition。

◎ 助動詞 may 和第 1 句一樣可作為「避險」之用。

◎ 另外，serve as a basis for the study of 是比較接近撰寫理論重要性的句型。

3 The simplicity of operation <u>should</u> <u>enable</u> the student <u>to</u> observe details required in all systems without the usual problem of having to learn complex operating procedures.

◎ 最後一句寫的也是實用價值，助動詞用 should，語感上比 may 強烈一些。

◎ 動詞 enable 的用法是「enable + 受詞 + to + 動詞」。

範例 1 句型

1. This is done with the hope that it may provide an alternative solution to the problem of ___本研究要解決的實務問題___ .

2. Additionally, ___本研究的成果___ may serve as a basis for the study of ___作為理論基礎的研究___ .

3. ___本研究的成果___ should enable ___某人或事物___ to ___帶來研究成果的效益___ .

練習

請按照以上講解說明以及你自己的研究內容，填入以下段落的空格來表達研究價值。

This is done with the hope that it may provide an alternative solution

to the problem of _____. Additionally,

_____ may serve as a basis for the study

of _____. _____

should enable _____ to

_____.

範例 2

研究缺口、研究目的和研究價值這三項元素因為彼此的語意和邏輯關係緊密，有時可以整合寫在同一個段落裡。如以下範例：

① However, one problem with this area of research is that most studies were conducted with participants who were still studying interpretation, making it difficult to apply the results to professional interpreters who regularly face the challenge of interpreting in both directions. ② Moreover, few studies so far have attempted to account for the role of language direction in the overall process of simultaneous interpreting. ③ The answer to such questions will not only have important pedagogical implications, but may also shed light on the different cognitive processes involved in the respective directions. ④ The aim of this paper, therefore, is to investigate the various strategies used by interpreters when interpreting in each direction.

然而，這類研究有個問題，就是大多數研究都是以口譯學習者為對象，難以將研究結果應用到經常得面對雙向口譯挑戰的專業口譯員身上。而且至今很少研究嘗試解釋語言方向在整個同步口譯過程的角色。回答這些問題不僅對教學有重要義涵，而且能闡明口譯不同方向的認知過程。因此本論文的目的在調查口譯員在口譯語言方向所使用的不同策略。

範例 2 講解

1 <u>However</u>, one problem with this area of research is that most studies were conducted with participants who were still studying interpretation, making it difficult to apply the results to professional interpreters who regularly face the challenge of interpreting in both directions.

- ◎ 第 1 句和第 2 句都是陳述研究領域的缺口，第 1 句於句首用表「然而」的連接副詞 however，帶出過去研究中研究對象的問題及其應用上的困難，也就暗示了此研究將避免相同的問題和困難。

- ◎ 句中的現在分詞片語 making it difficult to apply the results to... 帶出過去研究結果在應用上的困難。

2 <u>Moreover</u>, <u>few studies</u> so far <u>have attempted</u> to <u>account for</u> the role of language direction in the overall process of simultaneous interpreting.

- ◎ 第 2 句進一步講述第二個研究缺口，因此用連接副詞 moreover 來強調，也可代換成 furthermore, in addition 等。

- ◎ 此句指出目前該領域仍缺乏哪一種研究，用 few studies 表該研究非常之少。要記得 few 是接可數名詞 studies；如果要用不可數名詞 research，就要改成 little research。不過台灣同學常寫成 *few researches，是將 research 視為可數名詞的錯誤用法。

- ◎ 此句用現在完成式，在主詞 few studies 和動詞 have attempted 之間可插入片語 so far，強調到目前為止。

- ◎ 另外，account for 是很常用的動詞，表「解釋」。

3 The answer to such questions <u>will</u> <u>not only</u> have important pedagogical implications, <u>but</u> may <u>also</u> <u>shed light on</u> the different cognitive processes involved in the respective directions.

◎ 此句承接前兩句所講的研究缺口，而帶出此研究的價值，也就是解決之前研究缺口的問題後所產生的效益或價值。

◎ 此句用對等連接詞 not only ... but also 連結兩種研究價值。

◎ 其中片語 shed light on 表「闡明」某概念或事物，在論文寫作中常用，shed 也可代換成 throw。

4 The aim of this paper, <u>therefore</u>, is to investigate the various strategies used by interpreters when interpreting in each direction.

◎ 最後一句才寫研究目的，銜接之前提到的研究缺口和價值。

◎ 用表「因果關係」的連接副詞 therefore，顯示是因為這些研究缺口和價值，所以才需要執行此研究。但是 therefore 在此是置於主詞 the aim of this paper 與 be 動詞 is 之間，所以 therefore 前後都要加逗號，與第 1 句的連接副詞 however 和第 2 句的連接副詞 moreover 都是置於句首的方式不同，等於是增加一點寫作句構上的變化。

範例2 **句型**

1. However, one problem with this area of research is that ___第一個研究缺口___, making it difficult to apply the results to ___該問題所造成應用上的困難___.

2. Moreover, few studies so far have attempted to account for the role of ___第二個研究缺口___.

3. The answer to such questions will not only have important ___某領域的___ implications, but may also shed light on ___研究問題或困難___.

4. The aim of this paper, therefore, is to investigate ___本研究的目的___.

練習

請按照以上講解說明以及你自己的研究內容，填入以下段落的空格來表達研究缺口、研究價值和研究目的。

However, one problem with this area of research is that

_____, making it difficult to apply the results

to _____. Moreover, few studies so far have

attempted to account for the role of _____.

The answer to such questions will not only have important

_____ implications, but may also shed light on

_____. The aim of this paper, therefore, is to

investigate _____.

Overview of the Paper
論文章節概述

在論文第一章緒論快結束前，有些作者會加上一段或數段對整篇論文章節的概述，也就是對每個章節的內容作一簡單介紹，方便讀者了解即將讀到的各章節重點，先有一個整體的概念。不過並不是每一位作者都會寫這段章節概述，要看個人的寫作偏好或論文架構而定。

範例 1

以下是整篇論文章節的概述，基本架構是逐句說明每節的主題。本範例第 1 句先說明該文共分五節，之後每句就描述其中一節，全部共有六句。而整段的時態都是現在式。

① This paper is divided into five main sections. ② Section 1 provides some background information about the beginning of the project. ③ Section 2 outlines the design of the STA. ④ Section 3 discusses the development of the prototype of STTS, describing some of the problems encountered. ⑤ Section 4 presents a number of applications of STA and STTS. ⑥ Finally, section 5 outlines some plans for future development.

本文分為五節，第一節提供此研究緣起的一些背景資料。第二節概述 STA 的設計。第三節討論 STTS 原型的發展，並陳述過程中所碰到的一些問題。第四節呈現 STA 和 STTS 的一些應用。最後，第五節概述某些未來發展的計畫。

範例1 講解

1 This paper <u>is divided into</u> five main sections.

○ 第 1 句先寫這篇論文共分爲幾個主要章節，使用常用的片語 is divided into，語態爲被動。

2 Section 1 <u>provides</u> some background information about the beginning of the project.

○ 第 2 句之後逐句陳述各節的主要內容。

○ 第一節通常先寫研究的背景資訊。

○ 注意每句中動詞的使用，作者通常會用不同動詞來呈現一些變化，例如本句用 provide。

3 Section 2 <u>outlines</u> the design of the STA.

○ 此句爲第二節內容，動詞用 outline。

4 Section 3 <u>discusses</u> the development of the prototype of STTS, <u>describing</u> some of the problems encountered.

○ 此句爲第三節內容，動詞用 discuss，但因英文句子中的謂語動詞只能有一個，所以後半句用 describing... 現在分詞片語擴展句意，進一步說明此節的內容。

5 Section 4 <u>presents</u> a number of applications of STA and STTS.

○ 此句爲第四節內容，動詞用 present。

6 Finally, section 5 <u>outlines</u> some plans for future development.

◯ 此句爲第五節內容，用連接副詞 finally 提示這是最後一節，動詞用 outline。

範例1 句型

---

1. This paper is divided into ___全文共分幾節___ main sections.

. . . .

2. Section 1 provides some background information about ___研究名稱或主題___ .（第一節的主要內容）

. . . .

3. Section 2 outlines the design of ___研究工具 A___ .（第二節的主要內容）

. . . .

4. Section 3 discusses the development of ___研究工具 B___ , describing some of the problems encountered.（第三節的主要內容）

. . . .

5. Section 4 presents a number of applications of ___研究工具的應用___ .（第四節的主要內容）

. . . .

6. Finally, section 5 outlines some plans for ___未來研究發展___ .（第五節的主要內容）

. . . .

練習

請按照以上講解說明以及你自己的研究內容，填入以下段落的空格來撰寫論文章節的概述。

This paper is divided into _____ main

sections. Section 1 provides some background information about

_____. Section 2 outlines the design of

_____. Section 3 discusses the development

of _____, describing some of the problems

encountered. Section 4 presents a number of applications of

_____. Finally, section 5 outlines some plans

for _____.

範例 2

　　此範例與上個範例在寫作結構上非常相似，只有在介紹每節的內容上有所不同。基本架構仍是逐句說明每節的主題。第 1 句先說明該文共分四節，之後每句就描述其中一節。而整段的時態也都是現在式。

① The article is divided into **four** main sections. ② Section 1 briefly outlines some of the challenges facing **translator trainers** who need to **evaluate student translations** in an academic context. ③ Section 2 provides a brief introduction to **corpora and corpus analysis tools**. ④ Section 3 describes the general design of **an Evaluation Corpus**. ⑤ Section 4 provides an example of how **an Evaluation Corpus** can be constructed and used to help **a translation trainer evaluate student translations**.

本文分為四節，第一節簡單介紹翻譯教師所面臨的挑戰，他們必須在學術環境評量學生的譯文。**第二節對**語料庫和語料分析工具**提供簡要概論。第三節陳述評量語料庫的一般性設計。第四節提供例子，說明如何建構評量語料庫，並用以協助翻譯教師評量學生譯作。**

範例2 **講解**

1 The article is divided into four main sections.

　　◎ 第 1 句先寫全文共有幾個主要章節，用片語 is divided into。

2　Section 1 briefly <u>outlines</u> some of <u>the challenges facing</u> translator trainers <u>who</u> need to evaluate student translations in an academic context.

- 第 2 句之後也是逐句陳述各節的主要內容，動詞用 outline。
- 本句為第一節內容，先寫背景資訊，例如此句點出研究所要處理的問題。
- 注意句中「the challenges facing + 人 + who 形容詞子句」是論文中相當常見的句型，用來表達「某人所面臨的挑戰」。

3　Section 2 <u>provides</u> a brief introduction <u>to</u> corpora and corpus analysis tools.

- 此句為第二節內容，動詞用 provide。
- 注意 introduction 之後的介系詞通常用 to。

4　Section 3 <u>describes</u> the general design of an Evaluation Corpus.

- 此句為第三節內容，動詞用 describe。

5　Section 4 <u>provides</u> an example of how an Evaluation Corpus can be constructed and used to help a translation trainer evaluate student translations.

- 此句為第四節內容，動詞用 provide。

範例 2　句型

---

1. The article is divided into ＿＿全文共分幾節＿＿ main sections.

---

2. Section 1 briefly outlines some of the challenges facing ＿＿人＿＿
 who need to ＿＿做什麼事＿＿ in ＿＿何種情境＿＿.（第一節的主要內容）

---

3. Section 2 provides a brief introduction to ＿＿研究主題＿＿.（第二節的
 主要內容）

---

4. Section 3 describes the general design of ＿＿研究工具＿＿.（第三節的主
 要內容）

---

5. Section 4 provides an example of how ＿＿研究工具＿＿ can be
 constructed and used to help ＿＿研究工具的用途＿＿.（第四節的主要內容）

練習

請按照以上講解說明以及你自己的研究內容，填入以下段落的空格來撰寫論文章節的概述。

The article is divided into _____

main sections. Section 1 briefly outlines some of the challenges

facing _____ who need to

_____ in _____.

Section 2 provides a brief introduction to

_____. Section 3 describes the general design

of _____. Section 4 provides an example of

how _____ can be constructed and used to

help _____.

段落指引

Method

　　在論文所有的章節中，研究方法應該是最容易寫的一章，甚至是許多人最先寫的一章。寫研究方法基本上只要平鋪直述、客觀詳實呈現研究的方法和過程即可，不像撰寫緒論和討論兩章時需要較多主觀的詮釋和邏輯的論證。而撰寫研究方法的單純性也反映在時態的使用上，由於研究已在過去某個時點完成，因此寫作中提到該研究時都應該用過去式。不像在寫緒論和討論時，時態的轉移非常頻繁，常讓寫作者感到頭痛。

　　研究方法的寫作重點有兩項：一是執行研究的方法或步驟，二是過程中所使用的研究材料或工具。其他相關事項還包括研究的設計、對象、抽樣的方式、變項的種類、蒐集資料的程序、分析資料的方法等。以訪談為例，基本上可分為結構式訪談 (structured interview)、半結構式訪談 (semi-structured interview)、非結構式訪談 (unstructured interview)、焦點團體訪談 (focus group interview)、深度訪談 (in-depth interview)、面訪 (face-to-face interview) 和電話訪談 (telephone interview) 等，各自具有不同的研究功能和操作型式。在寫作時首先必須明確指出自己使用哪種訪談法，之後再描述訪談的對象、地點、時間、期間、過程、記錄和分析方式等各個步驟的細節。

　　寫作時除有篇幅限制外應力求詳盡，有些讀者可能有興趣根據你的研究方法來複製或延伸此研究，這也是對研究社群的一種貢獻。尤其在科學研究上，可複製性是一重要的要求，才能證明其研究結果是可信的 (reliable)，而對研究方法的詳細描述就是別人可複製該研究的基礎。相對地，如果研究方法寫得模糊簡略，

就算最後的研究結果很有意義，在投稿時審查委員覺得其研究方法不盡合理，仍會被退稿。

　　一般而言，研究方法的寫作可區分為以下五小節：
1. Research Design（研究設計）
2. Subjects/Participants（研究對象／參與者）
3. Materials/Instruments（研究材料／工具）
4. Data Collection Procedure（資料蒐集程序）
5. Data Analysis（資料分析）

　　雖然上述五小節寫作的邏輯是按照研究方法執行過程的順序，但寫作元素的安排仍應視研究的屬性和主題而定，沒有一成不變的模式。以下分節敘述之。

Research Design
研究設計

撰寫研究方法一開始就應該告訴讀者該研究是使用什麼方法,而更具體來說,量性研究方法還包括調查法 (survey)、實驗法 (experiment)、測驗 (testing) 等;而質性研究方法也包括人種誌研究 (ethnographic research)、訪談法 (interview)、觀察法 (observation)、個案研究 (case study) 等,都應該在研究設計中就先寫清楚,並提供大概的研究過程和使用材料等資訊。至於更詳實的研究執行細節就留在接下來的各小節中一一說明。

範例 1

此研究設計範例是從研究問題出發,依序寫出研究方法、工具和變項等資訊。

① The study was designed to answer the following research question: Do listeners perform significantly better on a test of listening comprehension in English when the speaker shares the listeners' native language? ② We investigated this question by constructing and administering a specially designed version of the listening section of the TOEFL, called the Listening Comprehension Test. ③ It included lectures delivered in English by NSs of four languages; participants taking the test represented the same language backgrounds. ④ The two independent variables were the listeners' native language and the speaker's native language. ⑤ The dependent variable was the score achieved on the Listening Comprehension Test.

本研究設計用以回答以下問題：在英語聽力測驗中，如果說話者懂得聆聽者的母語，那麼聆聽者的英語聽力表現**是否會**比較好？**我們透過編製和實施**一個特別設計的托福聽力測驗**來探討這個研究問題**。它包括由四名不同母語的說話者用英文所作的演講，而接受測驗的研究參與者則具有相同的語言背景。**研究的兩個自變項為**聆聽者的母語以及說話者的母語，**因變項為**聽力測驗所得的分數。

Method

範例 1 **講解**

1 The study was designed to answer the following research question: <u>Do</u> listeners perform significantly better on a test of listening comprehension in English when the speaker shares the listeners' native language?

- 首句先呈現研究問題，是以助動詞 do 開頭的封閉性問題。
- 之後的研究過程都是為回答此問題而設計，下文的撰寫也是環繞此問題而開展。

2 <u>We</u> investigated this question by <u>constructing</u> and <u>administering</u> a specially designed version of the listening section of the TOEFL, called the Listening Comprehension Test.

- 本句承接上句提出的研究問題，陳述如何執行該研究，最重要的就是 construct（編製）和 administer（施測）一個聽力測驗，這兩個動詞在撰寫問卷、測驗和實驗的研究過程時都相當常用。

◎ 作者用第一人稱代名詞 we 來指涉其研究團隊，若要用第三人稱則可改為 the researchers of this study。

3 It included lectures delivered in English by NSs of four languages; participants taking the test represented the same language backgrounds.

◎ 第 3 句補充說明第 2 句所提到的聽力測驗，也就是本研究所使用的研究工具。

◎ 句首代名詞 it 指的是前一句的 Listening Comprehension Test。

◎ 動詞 include 常用來描述研究工具的組成部分，可用 consist of 或 contain 代換。

◎ 本句有兩個子句，中間用分號隔開，表示兩句的語意關係緊密，而後句是在寫測驗的受測者，主詞用 participants。

4 The two independent variables were the listeners' native language and the speaker's native language.

◎ 接下來寫研究的變項，通常先寫自變項 (independent variable)。

5 The dependent variable was the score achieved on the Listening Comprehension Test.

◎ 最後一句再寫因變項 (dependent variable)。

1. The study was designed to answer the following research question:
   Do ___研究問題___?

2. We investigated this question by constructing and administering
   ___研究方法和工具___.

3. It included ___研究工具的組成部分___.

4. The ___自變項的數量___ independent variables were ___自變項 A___
   and ___自變項 B___.

5. The dependent variable was ___因變項___.

練習

請按照以上講解說明以及你自己的研究內容，填入以下段落的空格來撰寫
研究設計。

The study was designed to answer the following research question: Do

_____? We investigated this question by

constructing and administering _____.

It included _____. The

_____ independent variables were

_____ and _____.

The dependent variable was _____.

範例 2

　　以下範例是量性研究的實驗設計，基本上是依據研究的時程發展順序，從費時多久、經歷幾個階段、最後再加上訪談等資訊來撰寫。全段時態都是過去式。

① The experimental sequence of the study took approximately 4.5 hours spread over 1 month. ② The treatment consisted of **two phases**, with **two tasks in each phase**. ③ Each treatment was followed by a posttest. ④ In an attempt to minimize the test effects, Phase 1 began **a full week after the pretest**, and Phase 2 started **a week after Posttest 1**. ⑤ After each treatment phase, we randomly selected and interviewed **four students** to obtain retrospective data on **the cognitive processes**; logistical issues prevented us from interviewing all the participants.

研究的實驗程序費時約 4.5 個小時，為期共一個月。實驗處理由兩個階段所組成，每階段要從事兩個任務。每次實驗處理結束後都要後測。為降低測驗效應，在前測結束後一週才開始第一階段，而第一次後測結束一週後才執行第二階段。每次實驗處理完後，我們隨機挑選訪談四名學生，以取得他們回想認知過程的資料。但是在資源有限的情況下，我們無法訪談所有的參與者。

範例 2 講解

1 ┊ The experimental sequence of the study <u>took</u> approximately 4.5 hours spread over 1 month.

　◎ 首句先寫實驗程序所需時間和期間共爲時多久。

　◎ 動詞 take 可以代換成 last。

2 The treatment <u>consisted of</u> two phases, with two tasks in each phase.

◎ 再來寫實驗處理由幾個階段組成，表「組成」最常用動詞片語 consist of，要注意此片語沒有被動語態，也沒有進行式，不能寫成 *is consisted of 或 *is consisting of。

3 Each treatment <u>was followed by</u> a <u>posttest</u>.

◎ 接著繼續寫實驗處理完後的程序，也就是執行 posttest（後測），此字是複合字 (compound word)，也可以把前後兩個字拆開，中間用連字號 (hyphen) 連結，寫成 post-test。

◎ 動詞是用被動語態 was followed by，指的是 posttest 跟隨在 treatment 之後，或者說 treatment 被 posttest 跟隨。但有些人會誤認為 treatment 跟隨在 posttest 之後，解讀出來的意思剛好相反。

4 In an attempt to <u>minimize</u> the test effects, Phase 1 <u>began</u> a full week after the pretest, and Phase 2 <u>started</u> a week after Posttest 1.

◎ 考完第一次測驗後通常還會有印象，對再考第二次測驗的結果會有影響，這就叫作測驗效應 (test/testing effect)。但實驗必須降低此種效應，動詞用 minimize（最小化）就很貼切。

◎ 第一階段和第二階段的寫法是平行結構。但第一階段的動詞用 begin，而第二階段的動詞用 start，兩字意義相同，但用字就有變化。

5

After each treatment phase, we randomly selected and interviewed **four students** to obtain retrospective data on the cognitive processes; logistical issues prevented us from interviewing all the participants.

◎ 最後一句寫實驗處理結束後再進行訪談的對象人數和選取方式。一般而言，研究者不太可能訪談所有的研究對象，因此分號後面再加一句說明原因。

◎ 但是 logistical issues prevented us from interviewing all the participants 本身已是完整的句子，只是與之前的語意關係緊密，因此作者使用分號來銜接。其實也可以用句號斷開，再用大寫字母開頭獨立成一句：

• After each treatment phase, we randomly selected and interviewed four students to obtain retrospective data on the cognitive processes. Logistical issues prevented us from interviewing all the participants.

◎ 動詞 prevent（阻止）加上受詞 us 之後，注意還要加上介系詞 from。

範例 2 句型

1. The experimental sequence of the study took approximately ___實驗時數___ hours spread over ___整個實驗共耗時多久___ .

2. The treatment consisted of ___幾個（階段）___ phases, with ___幾個（任務）___ tasks in each phase.

3. Each treatment was followed by a posttest.

4. In an attempt to minimize the test effects, Phase 1 began ___從何時開始___ , and Phase 2 started ___從何時開始___ .

5. After each treatment phase, we randomly selected and interviewed ___幾位受測對象___ to obtain retrospective data on ___研究主題___ ; logistical issues prevented us from interviewing all the participants.

練習

請按照以上講解說明以及你自己的研究內容，填入以下段落的空格來撰寫實驗研究設計。

The experimental sequence of the study took approximately

_____ hours spread over

_____ . The treatment

consisted of _____ phases, with

_____ tasks in each phase. Each treatment

was followed by a posttest. In an attempt to minimize the test effects,

Phase 1 began _____, and Phase 2 started

_____ . After each treatment phase, we

randomly selected and interviewed _____ to

obtain retrospective data on _____; logistical

issues prevented us from interviewing all the participants.

範例 **3**

此範例主要在說明質性個案研究的特點和要求，先寫研究的方法和目的，再介紹質性研究方法的一般要求，最後再回到研究本身說明資料如何蒐集。整段的時態都是用過去式。

① This study employed a qualitative case study approach to gain an in-depth and holistic understanding of **learners' perspectives**. ② In keeping with a tradition in qualitative research, I aimed for thick descriptions of the individual cases, while also attempting to identify some general trends and significant patterns among them. ③ Achieving this goal required triangulation of multiple methods, data sources, and viewpoints. ④ The study documented the participants' thoughts and feelings about **everyday classroom practices** over an extended period of time, revealing **their struggles as well as personally significant transformations**.

此研究使用質性個案研究方法來取得對學習者觀點的深度和整體了解。為遵循質性研究的傳統，我的目標是對每個個案採詳實的描述，同時也嘗試辨識出一些普遍性的趨勢和有意義的模式。為達此目標需要採多種方法、資料來源和觀點的三角檢證。本研究長期記錄了參與者對於平日上課的想法和感受，顯示出他們的努力與個人的重要蛻變。

1 This study <u>employed</u> a qualitative case study approach to gain an in-depth and holistic understanding of learners' perspectives.

- 首句先寫出此研究使用的研究方法以及所要達到的研究目的。
- 動詞使用過去式的 employed，也可以代換成 used, adopted, utilized, applied 等字。

2 In keeping with a tradition in qualitative research, I aimed for <u>thick descriptions</u> of the individual cases, while also attempting to identify some <u>general trends</u> and <u>significant patterns</u> among them.

- 第 2 句是說明一般執行質性研究所希望達到的目標，包括 thick descriptions, general trends, significant patterns，相當適合用來撰寫所有的質性研究方法。

3 Achieving this goal required <u>triangulation</u> of multiple methods, data sources, and viewpoints.

- 第 3 句是為達到第 2 句設定的目標所必須採用的方式，也就是對資料蒐集方法、來源和分析觀點的三角檢證 (triangulation)，也等於是進一步說明質性研究方法的特性。

> **4** The study <u>documented</u> the <u>participants'</u> thoughts and feelings about **everyday classroom practices** over an extended period of time, revealing **their struggles as well as personally significant transformations**.

- ◎ 第 2 句和第 3 句其實都是在寫質性研究方法的一般性要求，最後一句才回到作者本身的研究，主要是講述資料的蒐集。
- ◎ 動詞用 document，也可以代換成 record。
- ◎ 參與研究者用 participant 一字表達，是質性研究常用的字眼。

範例 3　句型

1. This study employed a qualitative case study approach to gain an in-depth and holistic understanding of ____研究主題____.

2. In keeping with a tradition in qualitative research, I aimed for thick descriptions of the individual cases, while also attempting to identify some general trends and significant patterns among them.

3. Achieving this goal required triangulation of multiple methods, data sources, and viewpoints.

4. The study documented the participants' thoughts and feelings about ____研究主題____ over an extended period of time, revealing ____研究所得結果____.

練習

請按照以上講解說明以及你自己的研究內容，填入以下段落的空格來撰寫質性個案研究設計。

This study employed a qualitative case study approach to gain an in-depth and holistic understanding of _____.
In keeping with a tradition in qualitative research, I aimed for thick descriptions of the individual cases, while also attempting to identify some general trends and significant patterns among them. Achieving this goal required triangulation of multiple methods, data sources, and viewpoints. The study documented the participants' thoughts and feelings about _____ over an extended period of time, revealing _____.

Method

範例 4

以下範例為半結構式電話訪談的研究方法，作者描述其執行訪談的期間、時間、過程、記錄和分析方式。全段使用過去式時態和大量的被動語態。

---

① A semi-structured telephone interview method was chosen. ② The interviews were scheduled at individual **interpreters'** convenience, and were held over a period of 15 days from **late September** to **early October 2009.** ③ Interviews were limited to about **20** minutes, in consideration of **the interpreters'** busy schedules. ④ Reponses were noted on **survey sheets** and later coded for analysis. ⑤ Some responses, including those related to **the profile of interpreters**, were suitable for quantitative analysis, while responses to the open-ended questions required qualitative analysis.

本研究選擇半結構式電話訪談方法，按每位口譯員的方便來安排時間，從 2009 年的九月底到十月初共為期 15 天。**因考量口譯員非常忙碌，每次訪談只限** 20 分鐘。**訪談內容記錄在調查表上，之後再編碼作分析。有些內容，包括口譯者的背景資料，適合作量性分析；**有些回答開放性問題的內容則需要進行質性分析。

範例 4 **講解**

1 ┊ A semi-structured telephone interview method <u>was chosen</u>.

> ◎ 一開始先講使用何種方式的訪談，用過去式被動語態 was chosen，chosen 也可代換成 employed, used, adopted, utilized, applied 等字。

2 The interviews <u>were scheduled</u> at individual **interpreters'** convenience, and <u>were held</u> over a period of **15** days from **late September** to **early October 2009**.

- 這句寫訪談的天數和期間，用過去式被動語態 were scheduled 和 were held。

3 Interviews <u>were limited</u> to about **20** minutes, in consideration of **the interpreters'** busy schedules.

- 第 3 句寫每一次訪談的時間長度，用過去式被動語態 were limited。

4 Reponses <u>were noted</u> on **survey sheets** and later <u>coded</u> for analysis.

- 再來寫記錄資料的方式，使用兩個過去式被動語態的動詞 were noted 和 were coded，用 and 連接，而因可共用同一個 be 動詞 were，後面出現的動詞就只寫 coded 即可。

5 Some responses, <u>including</u> those related to **the profile of interpreters**, were suitable for quantitative analysis, <u>while</u> responses to the open-ended questions required qualitative analysis.

- 接下來寫訪談資料的分析方式，包括量性和質性的資料。
- 主詞 some responses 和動詞 were 之間插入現在分詞片語 including those related to...，這種寫法使資訊比較緊密而有變化。
- 最後一個子句由從屬連接詞 while 帶出說明質性資料如何分析。

範例4 **句型**

1. A ___訪談結講___ interview method was chosen.

2. The interviews were scheduled at individual ___受訪對象的___ convenience, and were held over a period of ___受訪天數___ days from ___何年何月何日___ to ___何年何月何日___ .

3. Interviews were limited to about ___訪談所花時間___ minutes, in consideration of ___受訪對象的___ busy schedules.

4. Reponses were noted on ___記錄訪談工具___ and later coded for analysis.

5. Some responses, including those related to ___受訪對象的背景資料___ , were suitable for quantitative analysis, while responses to the open-ended questions required qualitative analysis.

練習

請按照以上講解說明以及你自己的研究內容，填入以下段落的空格來撰寫訪談研究設計。

A _____ interview method

was chosen. The interviews were scheduled at individual

_____ convenience, and were held

over a period of _____ days from

_____ to _____.

Interviews were limited to about _____

minutes, in consideration of _____ busy

schedules. Reponses were noted on _____

and later coded for analysis. Some responses, including those related to

_____, were suitable for quantitative analysis,

while responses to the open-ended questions required qualitative

analysis.

此範例使用焦點團體訪談的研究方法，寫作重點在於團體成員的組成、人數、背景以及條件。整段都是使用過去式時態。

① The focus group described below consisted of interpreters from three CHIA chapters (Bay Area, Central Valley and Los Angeles). ② All were practicing healthcare interpreters with a minimum of three years of experience, who had agreed to express their opinions, thoughts and concerns regarding the *Standards*. ③ A total of fifty-three interpreters participated in this study. ④ Thirty-nine (73%) were female and fourteen (27%) male. ⑤ They were recruited from interpreting agencies and other health organizations. ⑥ The only requirement for participation was a minimum of three years' experience in a health setting.

以下所描述的焦點團體訪談，是由來自三個 CHIA 分會（灣區、中央山谷和洛杉磯）的口譯員所組成。所有參與者都是現職醫療口譯員，工作經驗至少三年，他們都同意來表達對 Standards 規章的意見想法和關切事項。總共有 53 位口譯員參與這項研究，其中有 39 位 (73%) 女性和 14 位 (27%) 男性。他們是由口譯中介和其他醫療機構招募而來。參與研究的唯一條件為至少擁有三年在醫療環境的口譯經驗。

範例5 **講解**

1 The focus group described below <u>consisted of</u> interpreters from **three** CHIA <u>chapters</u> (Bay Area, Central Valley and Los Angeles).

- 首句先講焦點團體成員的組成來源，用表「組成」的動詞片語 consist of。consist 是不及物動詞，後面一定要加介系詞 of。
- 句中 chapter 不是作一般「章節」解釋，而是指「分會」。

2 All were **practicing healthcare interpreters** with a minimum of **three** years of experience, who had agreed to express their opinions, thoughts and concerns regarding **the** *Standards*.

- 第 2 句介紹訪談對象的條件和訪談的主題。

3 <u>A total of</u> fifty-three interpreters <u>participated in</u> this study.

- 第 3 句寫訪談的總人數，常用片語「a total of + 人數」。
- 表「參與」的動詞片語 participate in 不能只寫 participate，因為該字為不及物動詞。

4 <u>Thirty-nine</u> (73%) <u>were</u> female and **fourteen** (27%) male.

- 此句描述研究參與者的性別分布，一般而言超過 10 以上的數字用阿拉伯數字書寫。但因此句是用數字作開頭，按寫作規範，句首向來需以文字型式呈現，所以作者使用 thirty-nine，而不用 39。

- 爲求一致，作者在全段的數字除了圓括號內的百分比使用阿拉伯數字之外（如句中的 73% 和 27%），其餘的數字皆以文字拼寫。

- 本句有兩個子句，主詞分別爲 thirty-nine 和 fourteen，按理也應有兩個 be 動詞，但因前後兩個 be 動詞都是相同功能的 were，爲求精簡，就省略第二個子句的 be 動詞 were，原文應爲 ...fourteen (27%) were male.。

5 They <u>were recruited</u> from interpreting agencies and other health organizations.

- 第 5 句寫招募訪談對象的來源，動詞用過去式被動語態 were recruited。

6 The only requirement for participation was a minimum of three years' experience in a health setting.

- 最後一句重複第 2 句中訪談對象的條件限制，強調這是唯一的限制條件。

1. The focus group described below consisted of ___訪談對象___ from ___訪談對象的來源___ .

2. All were ___訪談對象的背景___ with a minimum of ___幾年（的經驗）___ years of experience, who had agreed to express their opinions, thoughts and concerns regarding ___訪談的主題___ .

3. A total of ___總人數___ participated in this study.

4. ___（女性受訪者的）人數和百分比___ were female and ___（男性受訪者的）人數和百分比___ male.

5. They were recruited from ___招募來源___ .

6. The only requirement for participation was ___條件限制___ .

Method

練習

請按照以上講解說明以及你自己的研究內容，填入以下段落的空格來撰寫
焦點團體訪談設計。

The focus group described below consisted of

_____ from _____.

All were _____ with a minimum of

_____ years of experience, who had

agreed to express their opinions, thoughts and concerns regarding

_____. A total of

_____ participated in this

study. _____ were female and

_____ male. They were recruited from

_____. The only requirement for participation

was _____.

Subjects/Participants

研究對象 / 參與者

「研究對象」在英文論文寫作中有許多不同的名稱，量性研究向來都用 subject 一字，強調其外在客觀性。而質性研究早期也用 subject 一字，後來有人針對調查訪談的對象使用 interviewee（受訪者）或 respondent（應答者），而人類學研究中較常用 informant（提供資料者）。不過近年來表研究對象最為政治正確 (political correctness) 的用字則為 participant（參與者），此字較能凸顯研究參與者的主動涉入 (active involvement) 精神以及與研究者之間的平等關係，也顯示研究者對於參與研究人士的尊重。

撰寫研究對象的重要資訊包括人數、選取來源、資格和方式，以及這些人的背景資料。這些資訊可以幫助讀者判斷研究對象的背景和他們提供的資料是否能達到原先預期的研究目的，以及與研究結果之間的關係是否有效和可信。

範例 1

以下範例雖短，但包含三個重要資訊，分別是研究對象的人數和來源、選擇這些對象的理由和研究對象的背景屬性。全段都是用過去式時態。

① The subjects who volunteered to take part in the study were 240 American undergraduates enrolled at the University of Illinois. ② Undergraduates were chosen because they were considered to be peers of Arab students. ③ The sample included students from a wide range of academic areas.

自願參加此研究的對象為 240 名就讀伊利諾大學的美國大學生。**選擇大學生的理由是因為他們被視為是**阿拉伯學生的同儕。**這些樣本包括**來自各學術領域的學生。

範例1 講解

1 The <u>subjects</u> who volunteered to <u>take part in</u> the study were 240 American undergraduates enrolled at the University of Illinois.

◎ 首句通常寫參加研究的人數和來源，研究對象用 subjects。

◎ 表達「參與」研究的動詞除了用片語 take part in，也可以代換成 participate in。

2 Undergraduates <u>were chosen</u> because they were considered to be peers of Arab students.

◎ 第 2 句描寫選擇這些研究對象的原因，被動語態 were chosen 也可以代換成 were selected。

3 The <u>sample</u> included students from a wide range of academic areas.

◎ 此句再說明研究對象的背景屬性，作者把所有的研究對象視為一個樣本 (sample)，其實也就是第 1 句的 subjects。

1. The subjects who volunteered to take part in the study were ____（研究對象的）人數和來源___ .

2. ___研究對象___ were chosen because they were considered to be ___選擇研究對象的理由___ .

3. The sample included ___樣本的背景屬性___ .

Method

149

練習

請按照以上講解說明以及你自己的研究內容，填入以下段落的空格來撰寫
研究對象。

The subjects who volunteered to take part in the study were

_____. _____

were chosen because they were considered to be

_____. The sample included

_____.

範例 2

這個範例的資訊包含研究對象的人數、性別、語言背景、年齡和英文能力。全段時態用過去式。

---

① The participants (24 women, 6 men) were 10 native speakers each of Cantonese, Spanish, and Canadian English, ranging in age from 17 to 50 years ($M = 37.5$ years). ② Their scores on the Test of English as a Foreign Language (TOEFL) ranged from 543 to 650 ($M = 604$). ③ All reported extensive daily contact with English.

參與者（24 名女性和 6 名男性）是講廣東話、西班牙語和加拿大英語者各 10 人，年齡從 17 歲到 50 歲（平均年齡 37.5 歲）。他們的托福分數介於 543 分至 650 分之間（平均分數 604 分）。每個人都宣稱每天都大量接觸英語。

範例 2 講解

1 | The participants (24 women, 6 men) were 10 native speakers each of Cantonese, Spanish, and Canadian English, ranging in age from 17 to 50 years ($M = 37.5$ years).

- 先寫參與者的人數、性別和語言背景。
- 主詞使用 participants 通常為質性研究。
- 句子中已有 be 動詞 were，因此使用第二個動詞時就改用現在分詞 ranging 引導的片語，說明年齡分布的情形。

2 Their scores on the Test of English as a Foreign Language (TOEFL) <u>ranged from</u> 543 <u>to</u> 650 ($M = 604$).

- 第 2 句繼續描述參與者的特性，此研究的重要變項是參與者的英語程度，因此提供他們托福成績的資料。

- 動詞用過去式 ranged，該字一般是當名詞表「範圍」，但在論文寫作中常當動詞並和介系詞 from ... to... 連用，表「在某範圍內的變動」。

3 <u>All</u> reported extensive daily contact with English.

- 最後一句再寫參與者的背景，而且是以參與者自行報告的方式呈現。

- 句子主詞是代名詞 all，指所有參與者 (all participants)。

範例2 **句型**

1. The participants (___人數___ women, ___人數___ men) were ___參與者的背景___ , ranging in age from ___最年輕的年齡___ to ___最年長的年齡___ years ($M = $ ___平均年齡___ years).

2. Their ___參與者的特質___ ranged from ___特質的最低量___ to ___特質的最高量___ ($M = $ ___特質的平均量___).

3. All reported ___參與者對其特質的描述___ .

練習

請按照以上講解說明以及你自己的研究內容，填入以下段落的空格來撰寫研究參與者。

The participants (_____

women, _____ men) were

_____, ranging in age from

_____ to _____

years (*M* = _____ years).

Their _____ ranged from

_____ to _____

(*M* = _____). All reported

_____.

Materials/Instruments

研究材料／工具

研究材料或工具指的是蒐集研究資料過程中所使用的器材，例如實驗儀器、設備、問卷、測驗卷、訪談綱要、觀察表等。這些材料或工具的來源可能是採購標準化的器材、採用或修訂之前研究使用過的材料、或研究者自行創製研發等。

撰寫研究材料或工具時應包括取得來源或研製過程、主要的組成部分或規格以及使用的功能或方法。時態上大多是使用過去式，但如果是描述學界普遍使用的標準儀器設備或工具，則可以用現在式。至於語態則是以被動居多，可以減少主詞出現研究者的機會，降低人為的色彩。

範例 1

以下範例所描述的研究工具為問卷調查，包括受訪者的背景資料、選擇題和開放性問題等，共分為五大部分，需要對組成問卷的各個部分逐一說明。

---

① The questionnaire consisted of five sections, the first of which was intended to elicit demographic information on the respondents. ② The second section asked respondents to rate their degree of familiarity with statistical terms. ③ Section 3 focused on attitudes regarding the role of statistically based research. ④ The fourth section was designed to assess opinions of specific problem areas for which there is no consensus on appropriate procedures. ⑤ More open-ended research problems were presented in the fifth section, where respondents were asked how they would go about solving these problems and dealing with these data. ⑥ Finally, survey respondents were also asked to make general comments on the questionnaire.

此問卷由五大部分所組成，第一部分用以取得受訪者背景資料。第二部分請受訪者就自己對統計術語的熟悉程度評分。第三部分探究對統計研究所扮演角色的態度。第四部分評估受訪者對因缺乏適當程序的共識所產生的問題有何意見。第五部分則是開放性問題，請受訪者回答如何解決問題並處理這些資料。最後，請調查的受訪者對問卷提出一般性評論。

範例1 **講解**

1　The questionnaire <u>consisted of</u> five sections, <u>the first of which</u> was intended to elicit demographic information on the respondents.

- ◎ 第 1 句先講問卷由幾個部分組成，consist of 是最常用的動詞片語，也可代換成 be comprised of。
- ◎ 逗號後是一個非限定關係子句，以 the first of which 作為主詞。which 是指前面的先行詞 five sections，因此 the first of which 就是 the first of the five sections，亦即問卷的第一部分。
- ◎ 問卷的第一部分通常都是調查受訪者的背景資料，因此這句除了修改問卷組成部分的數量之外，基本上可以直接引用到大部分的問卷寫作上。

2　The second section <u>asked</u> respondents to rate their degree of familiarity with statistical terms.

- ◎ 第 2 句之後逐句說明問卷各組成部分的內容或目的。

155

◎ 此句要求受訪者作程度上的評分，注意它是用主動語態 asked，因為主詞是問卷，而不是研究者，不致有人為的主觀色彩。

3 Section 3 <u>focused on</u> attitudes <u>regarding</u> the role of statistically based research.

◎ 第 3 句也是用主動語態 focused on。

◎ regarding 是常用的介系詞，引介出此部分問卷的內容或主題，可以代換成 concerning。

4 The <u>fourth</u> section <u>was designed</u> to assess opinions of specific problem areas for which there is no consensus on appropriate procedures.

◎ 第 4 句說明問卷的第四部分，注意 fourth 的拼法，很多人用電腦寫作常打成 *forth 而不自覺。

◎ 這句是用被動語態 was designed。

5 More open-ended research problems <u>were presented</u> in the fifth section, <u>where</u> respondents <u>were asked</u> how they would go about solving these problems and dealing with these data.

◎ 這句也是用被動語態 were presented 和 were asked。

◎ 逗號後的子句是由關係副詞 where 所引導的形容詞子句來修飾其前的先行詞 the fifth section，說明問卷第五部分問題的內容。

156

6 <u>Finally</u>, survey respondents <u>were</u> also <u>asked</u> to make general comments on the questionnaire.

◎ 最後一句用連接副詞 finally 開頭，繼續說明第五部分的問題，此句也是用被動語態 were asked。

範例 1 句型

1. The questionnaire consisted of ___數量___ sections, the first of which was intended to elicit demographic information on the respondents.

2. The second section asked respondents to rate their degree of ___問卷第二部分的內容或主題，與評估程度有關___.

3. Section 3 focused on attitudes regarding ___問卷第三部分的內容或主題，與評估態度有關___.

4. The fourth section was designed to assess opinions of ___問卷第四部分的內容或主題，與評估意見有關___.

5. More open-ended research problems were presented in the fifth section, where respondents were asked ___問卷第五部分的內容或主題，是開放性問題___.

6. Finally, survey respondents were also asked to ___對問卷第五部分再提出評論___.

練習

請按照以上講解說明以及你自己的研究內容，填入以下段落的空格來撰寫問卷調查的組成部分。

The questionnaire consisted of _____

sections, the first of which was intended to elicit demographic information

on the respondents. The second section asked respondents to rate

their degree of _____. Section 3 focused on

attitudes regarding _____. The fourth section

was designed to assess opinions of _____.

More open-ended research problems were presented in the fifth section,

where respondents were asked _____. Finally,

survey respondents were also asked to _____.

範例 2

　　以下範例所使用的研究工具為標準化測驗，需要對組成測驗的各個部分逐一說明。因為是描述一份普遍使用的標準化試卷，全段時態都用現在式。

---

① The MTELP is a standardized measure designed to **predict academic success of international students at American universities**. ② The test consists of 100 items and is divided into **three** parts. ③ Part I contains 40 questions on grammar; Part II contains 30 questions on vocabulary; and Part III contains 30 questions testing **reading comprehension**.

MTELP 是種標準化測量工具，設計目的為預測國際學生就讀美國大學的學業成就。該測驗由 100 題所組成，分為三部分。第一部分包含 40 題文法題，第二部分包含 30 題字彙題，第三部分則包含 30 題閱讀測驗題。

範例 2 講解

1 The MTELP <u>is</u> a standardized measure <u>designed</u> to predict academic success of international students at American universities.

　　第 1 句寫出此測驗工具的用途。首先要寫出測驗工具的名稱，通常工具的全名較長，寫作上傾向用頭字詞 (acronym)，也就是由全名中每個字的第一個字母所組成，如本句中的 MTELP 就是 Michigan Test of English Language Proficiency 的頭字詞。

○ 全句的動詞是現在式的 is，雖然句中的 designed 看起來也像是動詞，但其實是過去分詞，這是一種簡化的寫法。原來的句子是 ...a standardized measure which is designed to...，但為了讓文意更緊湊，可以省略關係代名詞 which 和之後的 be 動詞 is，就變成本句中的形式。

2 The test <u>consists of</u> 100 items and <u>is divided into</u> three parts.

○ 第 2 句開始寫此測驗工具是由什麼所組成，consist of 是最常用的動詞片語，只有主動語態的用法。

○ 但句中後半部表達「被區分成…」時則要用被動語態，寫成 is divided into。

3 Part I <u>contains</u> 40 questions on grammar<u>;</u> Part II <u>contains</u> 30 questions on vocabulary<u>; and</u> Part III <u>contains</u> 30 questions testing reading comprehension.

○ 第 3 句則是說明測驗工具的各個組成部分。

○ 這句其實是由三句所組成，以分號代替句號來銜接三個句子，形成「句子 1 ; 句子 2 ; and 句子 3 .」的句型。

○ 各部分表「包含」的動詞都用 contain，也可用 include 來代換。

句型

1. ____測驗工具名稱____ is a standardized measure designed to ____測驗的用途或目的____ .

2. The test consists of ____題數____ items and is divided into ____幾（部分）____ parts.

3. Part I contains ____題數____ questions on ____第一部分測驗的內容或主題____ ; Part II contains ____題數____ questions on ____第二部分測驗的內容或主題____ ; and Part III contains ____題數____ questions testing ____第三部分測驗的內容或主題____ .

練習

請按照以上講解說明以及你自己的研究內容，填入以下段落的空格來撰寫
測驗用的工具。

_____ is a standardized measure

designed to _____. The test consists of

_____ items and is divided

into _____ parts. Part I

contains _____ questions

on _____; Part II contains

_____ questions on

_____; and Part III contains

_____ questions testing

_____.

Data Collection Procedure
資料蒐集程序

資料蒐集的過程換個方式來說就是執行研究的過程，不論是使用何種研究方法，例如實驗、調查、測驗、觀察、訪談等，都需要透過上一節描述的研究材料或工具來進行實徵資料 (empirical data) 的蒐集，也才能從事下一步的資料分析和詮釋。

撰寫時需要詳細交待蒐集資料的時間、地點、參與者和過程中的每一步驟。如果實施的過程很複雜，也可以加上流程圖 (flow chart) 或其他圖表來輔助說明。寫作時態仍偏向使用過去式，因為資訊蒐集程序在之前已經結束；語態則以被動居多，希望能降低個人主觀色彩，但質性研究則不在此限。

範例 1

此範例是以測驗為蒐集資料的程序，在測驗之前還先使用問卷來篩選受測者。以下段落包括時間、挑選受測者的方式和基本步驟等資訊。

---

① Data collection took place between February 2008 and August 2009. ② Before testing, potential participants filled in a questionnaire which asked about professional experience, education, language skills, and so on. ③ This questionnaire enabled us to verify that the participants met the selection criteria and to gather additional data which might be of interest for subsequent analysis.

④ Subjects were tested individually in two sessions, in order to avoid fatigue. ⑤ All told, the procedure took approximately **three hours for each subject.** ⑥ The order of presentation in the two sessions was as follows:

......

資料蒐集期間為 2008 年 2 月到 2009 年 8 月。**在測驗之前,可能參與研究的人士先填寫問卷,**以了解其專業經驗、教育程度、語言技能等。**此問卷能幫我們查核研究參與者是否符合選取條件,並取得額外的資料,**可能有助於後續的分析。

研究對象個別受測,分兩次進行,以避免過於疲憊。**每位受測者的整個測驗過程大約 3 小時。**而兩次受測的次序如下:

......

範例1 **講解**

1   Data collection <u>took place</u> between February 2008 and August 2009.

◯ 第 1 句先寫蒐集資料的期間,動詞用 took place,在描述過去蒐集資料的過程時都要用過去式。

2   Before testing, potential participants filled in a questionnaire <u>which</u> asked about professional experience, education, language skills, and so on.

◯ 第 2 句陳述在測驗前需要先填問卷,在 questionnaire 後使用 which 引導的形容詞子句來描述問卷的內容。

3 This questionnaire enabled us <u>to verify that</u> the participants met the selection criteria and <u>to gather</u> additional data <u>which</u> might be <u>of interest</u> for subsequent analysis.

- 第 3 句描述問卷的兩個功能,分別用「to verify + that 名詞子句」和「to gather data + which 形容詞子句」來呈現。注意連接詞 that 可以放在名詞子句或形容詞子句之前,要看它在整個子句的功能來判斷應該是接何種子句。例如在 to verify 之後要接名詞,因此 that 是引導名詞子句當作 to verify 的受詞。至於 to gather data which 其後是引導形容詞子句,來修飾先行的名詞 data。

- 句中的片語 of interest 也可代換爲 interesting,但因論文文體比較正式,傾向將其他詞性名詞化 (nominalization),因此把形容詞 interesting 寫成名詞化的 of interest。其他常見例子還有將 be very important 寫成 be of considerable importance,將 to apply 寫成 the application of,將 for a long time 寫成 for a considerable length of time 等,感覺比較正式,但也比較冗贅。

4 <u>Subjects were tested</u> individually in <u>two</u> sessions, in order to avoid fatigue.

- 第 4 句開始寫測驗的過程,因爲不同於前面幾句都在講問卷,所以作者就從這句另立新的一段。

- 句中用被動語態 subjects were tested...。subjects 與前幾句中的 participants 都是指「受測對象」。

5 | <u>All told</u>, the procedure <u>took</u> approximately three hours for each subject.

◎ 句首片語 all told 原意是「總計」，在此指整個施測時間。

◎ 動詞 take 可代換成 last。

6 | The order of presentation in the two sessions was <u>as follows</u>:

◎ 句尾 as follows 意指「如下所述」，注意這是固定用法，follow 一定要加 s，不能用 *as follow，也不可誤寫為 *as following，但可以代換成 as the following。

◎ 此句之後就開始詳述測驗的過程，但因資訊較為瑣細，難以歸納句型，於此略過。

1. Data collection took place between ___開始時間___ and ___結束時間___.

2. Before testing, potential participants filled in a questionnaire which asked about ___問卷的內容___.

3. This questionnaire enabled us to verify that the participants met the selection criteria and to gather additional data which might be of interest for subsequent analysis.

4. Subjects were tested individually in ___測驗的形式___.

5. All told, the procedure took approximately ___所需時間___ for each subject.

6. The order of presentation in ___測驗的形式___ was as follows:

練習

請按照以上講解說明以及你自己的研究內容，填入以下段落的空格來撰寫
測驗資料蒐集的過程。

Data collection took place between _____

and _____. Before testing, potential

participants filled in a questionnaire which asked about

_____. This questionnaire enabled us to verify

that the participants met the selection criteria and to gather additional

data which might be of interest for subsequent analysis.

Subjects were tested individually in _____. All

told, the procedure took approximately _____

for each subject. The order of presentation in

_____ was as follows:

......

範例 2

此範例是針對兩位教師的課堂教學來蒐集質性資料，需撰寫蒐集資料的期間、資料的來源和執行的人士。

① Data collection for this study occurred over 4 months. ② The sources of data included daily observation of Jenny and Sonya's classes, scheduled interviews, a videotape of one class session, and stimulus recall reports of the videotapes. ③ I conducted the observations, the interviews, and the stimulus recall individually with each teacher.

本研究的資料蒐集為期超過四個月。**資料來源包括**每日對 Jenny 和 Sonya 的課堂觀察、計畫訪談、一堂課的錄影以及錄影後的刺激回憶報告。**都是由我和**每位教師**執行**觀察、訪談和刺激回憶。

範例 2 講解

1 Data collection for this study <u>occurred</u> over 4 months.

- 第 1 句首先說明資料蒐集的期間有多長，動詞使用過去式的 occurred，也可以用 lasted 代換。

2 The sources of data <u>included</u> daily observation of Jenny and Sonya's classes, scheduled interviews, a videotape of one class session, and stimulus recall reports of the videotapes.

- 第 2 句寫資料的來源和種類，動詞用過去式的 included。

3 I <u>conducted</u> the observations, the interviews, and the stimulus recall individually with each teacher.

◎ 最後寫是由誰來執行資料蒐集過程，作者用第一人稱 I，在質性研究中較常用。

◎ 動詞用過去式的 conducted，也可以代換爲 did。

範例 2 句型

1. Data collection for this study occurred over ____一段期間____.

2. The sources of data included ____資料的來源和種類____.

3. I conducted ____執行資料蒐集的過程____ individually with ____研究對象____.

練習

請按照以上講解說明以及你自己的研究內容，填入以下段落的空格來撰寫蒐集質性研究資料的過程。

Data collection for this study occurred over

_____. The sources of data

included _____. I conducted

_____ individually with

_____.

Data Analysis
資料分析

　　撰寫資料分析時要詳述分析資料的方法，而且依量性和質性研究取向的不同，使用的分析方式也有很大的差異。首先在量性分析上一定要說明使用何種統計方法，除了描述性統計 (descriptive statistics) 要提供平均數 (mean)、標準差 (standard deviation) 等數據外，推論性統計 (inferential statistics) 也要表明是如何使用如 t 檢定 (t-test)、變異數分析 (ANOVA)、卡方檢定 (chi-square test) 或相關性分析 (correlation) 等方法。而質性分析最常使用分類 (categorization) 方式分析，其他還有紮根理論 (grounded theory)、語篇分析 (discourse analysis)、內容分析 (content analysis) 等分析方法，都要加以說明清楚。

　　一般在寫作時分析工作已經結束，所以動詞時態都是用過去式。至於在陳述上傾向用被動語態，以降低人為操作的語氣，也是去個人化 (depersonalized) 的寫作機制。這種現象在量性研究分析時特別明顯，如下句：

- Descriptive statistics were calculated.
  描述統計被計算。

但如果用主動語態，而且以第一人稱 I 作為主詞，如下句：

- I calculated descriptive statistics.
  我計算描述統計。

以第一人稱作主詞的寫法讓人感覺作者在強調自己的地位，但別人來計算是否就會有不同的答案呢？當然我們不希望不同的人來計算統計會得到不同的數據，所以在寫作上也就盡量降低個人主觀的色彩。

可是在質性研究上，有些分析方式的撰寫反而是要凸顯研究者的地位，習慣上用第一人稱來自稱。這是因為質性資料如訪談的逐字稿 (transcripts) 或現場筆記 (fieldnotes) 在記錄和分析上都相當主觀，同樣一份逐字稿交給不同人作編碼分析和詮釋，很可能會得到不盡相同的結果。在研究者必須為自己的分析結果負責下，用第一人稱也就是很自然的事。

範例 1

此研究使用三個統計分析方法，分別處理三個不同研究問題，用分項分行的方式撰寫比較清楚易讀。而且全部都是用過去式時態撰寫。

---

① Three types of statistical analyses were used:

② (1) The independent t-test was used to examine the differences between the group means on the intelligibility and naturalness judgments of grammatically deviant utterances.

③ (2) Three 2 x 2 univariate analyses of variance were performed to investigate the effect of error type and context on the three measures of intelligibility, naturalness, and interpretation.

④ (3) Fisher's Exact Test was used to investigate the relationship between the subjects' performance on the two measures of intelligibility and interpretation.

本研究使用三種統計分析方式：

(1) **使用**獨立 t 檢定**來檢視**兩組對不合文法口語的理解性和自然性判斷上平均數**的差異。**

(2) **執行**三個 2 x 2 單變量變異數分析**來探討**錯誤類型和文境對於理解性、自然性和詮釋性三個測量方式**的效果。**

(3) **使用** Fisher's Exact 檢定**來探討**受測對象在理解性和詮釋性兩種測量方式表現**的關係。**

範例1 **講解**

1 | Three types of statistical <u>analyses were used</u>:

- 首句指出要使用幾種統計方法，時態用過去式被動語態 were used，而 used 可以代換成 conducted, carried out, performed, undertaken。

- 因為有多種分析方式，「分析」要用複數型的 analyses，若是單數則用 analysis，兩字拼法非常接近。

2 | (1) The independent t-test <u>was used to examine</u> the differences between the group means on the intelligibility and naturalness judgments of grammatically deviant utterances.

- 本句亦是用過去式被動語態 was used，動詞 used 也可以代換成 employed, conducted, calculated, performed 等。

- 不定詞片語 to examine 也可以代換成 to investigate, to explore 等。

3

(2) Three 2 x 2 univariate analyses of variance <u>were performed</u> <u>to investigate the effect of</u> error type and context <u>on</u> the three measures of intelligibility, naturalness, and interpretation.

◎ 本句亦是用過去式被動語態 were performed，其後接不定詞片語 to investigate。

◎ 要表達「探討 A 對 B 的效果」可寫成 to investigate the effect of A on B。

4

(3) Fisher's Exact Test <u>was used</u> <u>to investigate</u> the relationship between the subjects' performance on the two measures of intelligibility and interpretation.

◎ 本句亦是用過去式被動語態 was used，其後接不定詞片語 to investigate。

範例 1　**句型**

1. ＿＿＿幾種（統計方法）＿＿＿ types of statistical analyses were used:

2. (1) ＿＿＿第一種統計方法＿＿＿ was used to examine the differences

   between ＿＿＿第一種統計方法要檢定事項的差異＿＿＿ .

3. (2) ＿＿＿第二種統計方法＿＿＿ were performed to investigate the effect of

   ＿＿＿第二種統計方法要檢定事項的效果＿＿＿ .

4. (3) ＿＿＿第三種統計方法＿＿＿ was used to investigate the relationship

   between ＿＿＿第三種統計方法要檢定事項的關係＿＿＿ .

練習

請按照以上講解說明以及你自己的研究內容，填入以下段落的空格來撰寫統計分析的方法。

_____ types of statistical analyses were used:

(1) _____ was used to examine the differences

between _____.

(2) _____ were performed to investigate the

effect of _____.

(3) _____ was used to investigate the

relationship between _____.

範例 **2**

　　以下整段質性分析的範例幾乎可適用於大部分的訪談分析過程，強調不斷地重新檢視所分析的資料，反映受訪者的觀點。整段採用過去式時態撰寫。

---

① During the analysis, I read through the interview transcripts, summarizing the informants' views, grouping these summaries, and describing them more precisely under headings. ② The data were then reexamined in their entirety and coded. ③ During coding, the headings were revised and refined to more accurately reflect the data, and these categories were renamed to reflect the nature of the informants' comments more precisely.

在分析過程中，我詳讀訪談的逐字稿，總結受訪者的觀點並作分類，再於標題下更精確地描述這些分類。之後我再重新檢視整體資料並加以編碼。在編碼過程中，我再重新修訂標題，俾使它們能更精確反映資料，而類別也重新命名以更精確反映受訪者的評論。

範例2 **講解**

1　During the analysis, I read through the interview transcripts, summarizing the informants' views, grouping these summaries, and describing them more precisely under headings.

◎ 首句描述作者分析過程的幾個步驟，此文用第一人稱 I 來指稱自己，在質性研究中常用。

- 動詞 read 看起來像現在式，但其實是過去式，因為 read 的現在式、過去式和過去分詞都是相同拼法。

- 此句中只用一個謂語動詞，雖然分析過程中還有許多動作，但句型上用現在分詞 summarizing..., grouping..., describing... 來表現一系列的行為，也是一種平行結構的寫法。

- 受訪者除了 informant，也可以使用 participant, interviewee, subject, respondent 等字取代，但每個字所代表的涵義稍有不同。

2　The data <u>were</u> <u>then</u> <u>reexamined</u> in their entirety <u>and</u> <u>coded</u>.

- 第 2 句中有連接副詞 then，也可以寫在句首成為 Then, the data were reexamined...。

- 動詞是兩個過去式被動語態 were reexamined 和 were coded，中間用連接詞 and 連接，而第二個 were 因重複可以省略，只剩下 coded。

3　During coding, the headings <u>were revised and refined</u> to more <u>accurately reflect</u> the data, <u>and</u> these categories <u>were renamed</u> to <u>reflect</u> the nature of the **informants'** comments more <u>precisely</u>.

- 第 3 句寫編碼過程，一樣使用過去式被動語態 were revised and refined 和 were renamed，以連接詞 and 連接。

- 句中兩個副詞 accurately 和 precisely 都是在修飾動詞 reflect。

1. During the analysis, I read through the interview transcripts, summarizing the ___研究對象的___ views, grouping these summaries, and describing them more precisely under headings.

2. The data were then reexamined in their entirety and coded.

3. During coding, the headings were revised and refined to more accurately reflect the data, and these categories were renamed to reflect the nature of the ___研究對象的___ comments more precisely.

練習

請按照以上講解說明以及你自己的研究內容，填入以下段落的空格來撰寫
質性訪談資料分析。

During the analysis, I read through the interview transcripts, summarizing

the _____ views, grouping these summaries,

and describing them more precisely under headings. The data were

then reexamined in their entirety and coded. During coding, the

headings were revised and refined to more accurately reflect the

data, and these categories were renamed to reflect the nature of the

_____ comments more precisely.

範例 **3**

　　以下範例是輔助量性問卷調查結果的質性訪談分析。通常問卷調查的結果有其限制，只能蒐集到研究對象用數字呈現對於問卷題目的回應，大多流於表面而無法得知研究對象比較深層或內心的想法。因此執行問卷調查之後，再針對特定的對象作訪談，可以獲取更深入的資料，也能進一步驗證問卷資料本身的有效性和可信度。

① The interview data were intended to serve as an additional source of information to validate the questionnaire survey. ② I read all the transcripts first. ③ On a second read, I identified salient excerpts that illustrated the interviewees' beliefs about **English learning**. ④ This information would be discussed as examples of **students' learning process** and be used to triangulate **students'** responses to the written questionnaires.

此訪談資料是用以證實問卷調查結果的另一種資料來源。我先閱讀過所有謄錄的逐字稿，在第二次閱讀時我辨識出一些特別的摘錄文字，顯示受訪者對於英語學習的信念。這些資訊會作為學生學習過程的例證來討論，也可用來三角檢測學生對書面問卷的回答。

範例 3　**講解**

1　The interview data <u>were intended</u> to serve as an additional source of information to validate the questionnaire survey.

　　◎ 首句先寫執行訪談的目的，主要是用來輔助量性的問卷調查結果，動詞用過去式被動語態 were intended。

2   I <u>read</u> all the transcripts first.

○ 第 2 句開始寫質性分析的過程，第一步是先閱讀逐字稿。

○ 使用第一人稱 I，動詞為過去式 read。

3   On a second <u>read</u>, I <u>identified</u> salient excerpts <u>that</u> illustrated the interviewees' beliefs about **English learning**.

○ 第 3 句繼續寫質性分析的程序，在此是做第二次閱讀，read 變成名詞。

○ 主詞使用第一人稱 I，動詞就不需要用被動語態，直接用主動語態 identified。

○ 句中有一關係代名詞 that 所引導的形容詞子句來修飾其先行詞 excerpts。

4   This information <u>would be discussed</u> as examples of students' learning process <u>and be used</u> to triangulate students' responses to the written questionnaires.

○ 最後一句呼應第 1 句，講這些資料的具體用途。

○ 主詞 this information 之後接兩個平行的被動語態動詞 would be discussed 和 would be used，中間用 and 連接。而第二個 would 可以省略，就只剩下 be used。

1. The interview data were intended to serve as an additional source of information to validate the questionnaire survey.

2. I read all the transcripts first.

3. On a second read, I identified salient excerpts that illustrated the interviewees' beliefs about ___研究主題___ .

4. This information would be discussed as examples of ___研究主題___ and be used to triangulate ___研究對象的___ responses to the written questionnaires.

練習

請按照以上講解說明以及你自己的研究內容，填入以下段落的空格來撰寫輔助問卷調查的訪談分析。

The interview data were intended to serve as an additional source of information to validate the questionnaire survey. I read all the transcripts first. On a second read, I identified salient excerpts that illustrated the interviewees' beliefs about _____.

This information would be discussed as examples of

_____ and be used to triangulate

_____ responses to the written questionnaires.

Research Results

　　研究結果是整個研究的核心，之前辛苦從事的文獻回顧和研究過程就是為了得到符合研究目的的結果，而之後的討論也是要基於這些結果才能產生意義。不過無論實際研究的結果是否令人滿意，此章的撰寫主要就在呈現研究方法執行後所得到的成果，而且和研究方法一樣都是相對比較好寫的章節。

　　本章的內容訊息比較單純，只要將研究所得的結果如實報告出來。而時態因研究結果已經在過去某一時點取得，全章大致保持在過去式，沒有太大的變化。不過如果有些作者喜歡將研究結果和針對結果的討論合併寫在一起，那整章的篇幅和寫作難度就會提升。一般而言，為了讓論文各章各自保持明確的訊息任務，詳盡的討論還是寫在論文最後一章比較清楚。此章仍以研究結果為主，再加上一些對這些結果的簡短評論 (comments) 或彙總 (summary) 即可。

　　再者，有些研究的結果比較龐雜，如受到期刊論文篇幅的限制，就只能報告最重要、最有意義的發現，其他結果可放在文後的附錄 (Appendix) 中而無需加以討論。另外，研究結果通常會加上許多圖表來輔助文字的陳述，因此圖表的製作與說明也很重要。

　　本章的內容相對單純，沒有固定的小節標題，但寫作的元素可簡單分為以下兩種：

1. Research Findings（研究發現）

2. Graphics and Locations of Results（圖表與研究結果所在）

　　每篇論文所寫研究結果的格式都不盡相同，是否會用圖表呈現也有差異。以下將依研究的類型如量性或質性的結果分別論述之。

Research Findings
研究發現

撰寫研究發現時，通常還需將整個研究的過程或分析方法再大致描述一下，讓讀者了解之前的資料是如何取得。接著量性研究會將結果的重點放在數據的呈現和統計的顯著性上，必須要報告確切的數據和解釋這些數據所代表的意義。而質性研究則多以文字來陳述結果，並依內容屬性區分許多小節，篇幅相對會比較長。時態基本上都是用過去式，只有論及一般事實或對研究結果作總結時，才可能轉用現在式。

範例 1

本範例撰寫問卷調查的結果，以受訪者回應的次數 (frequency) 和百分比 (percentage) 等描述性統計數據來呈現。但若只是用相同句型逐題報告數據會讓讀者覺得千篇一律，以下段落就嘗試做一些變化。例如研究對象有時用respondents，有時用 students，有時則乾脆省略；而動詞用了agreed, expressed, stated, said 等字；句型上有先報告數據再寫結果，也有先寫結果再報告數據。

① Ninety-one percent of all respondents agreed that they wanted to learn to speak English very well. ② The majority of students (78%) also associated the ability to speak English with better job opportunities. ③ These students also expressed a strong desire for friendships with Americans. ④ Almost 90% stated that they would like to have American friends, and over half said that they would like to learn English so that they can get to know Americans better. ⑤ It seems, then, that this group of students is strongly motivated to learn English and have both instrumental and integrative reasons for doing so.

有 91% 的應答者同意想要把英文學好。大多數學生 (78%) 也認為口說英文能力與更好的工作機會息息相關。這些學生也表達與美國人交朋友的強烈意願。幾近 90% 的人表示他們想要結交美國友人，也有超過半數的人表示想要學好英文才能更加了解美國人。這似乎顯示這群學生的英文學習動機很強，具有工具性和整合性的理由來學習英文。

範例1 講解

1 Ninety-one percent of all respondents agreed that they wanted to learn to speak English very well.

- ◎ 句首第一個字不宜用阿拉伯數字，因此用文字拼寫 ninety-one percent，但是文中其他百分比數字就可用阿拉伯數字表示。
- ◎ 填寫問卷的人可用 respondent（應答者）表示，動詞則用過去式 agreed。

2 The majority of students (78%) also associated the ability to speak English with better job opportunities.

- ◎ 在撰寫問卷結果時，不一定需要一直用數據呈現，有時可用文字詮釋。例如本句就用 the majority of students（大多數學生）來表示，而把 78% 置於圓括號內當作附屬的資訊，增加寫作的變化。
- ◎ 陳述應答者意見的動詞用 associate A with B。

3 These students also <u>expressed</u> a strong desire for friendships with Americans.

◎ 第 3 句其實是在爲第 4 句鋪路，先把調查學生的意見講出來，下一句才寫此結果的具體數據，這也是一種寫作的變化。

◎ 陳述應答者意見的動詞用 express。

4 Almost <u>90%</u> <u>stated</u> that they would like to have American friends, <u>and</u> over <u>half</u> <u>said</u> that they would like to learn English so that they can get to know Americans better.

◎ 第 4 句承接上句結果來提供具體數據，但作者省略回答問卷的主體，原本應該寫 90% of the students/respondents，但在此只寫 90%。

◎ 其後用 and 連接的子句亦是如此，作者只寫 half，而未寫 half of the students。

◎ 陳述應答者意見的動詞用 state 和 say。

5 It <u>seems</u>, then, that this group of students <u>is</u> strongly motivated to learn English and <u>have</u> both instrumental and integrative reasons for doing so.

◎ 最後一句要作總結，但對問卷調查結果的任何結論都無法百分之百肯定，因此要做論述上的「避險」，而此句就是用動詞 seem（似乎），讓主張的強度保守謹愼一些。

◎ 此句是作總結，屬於普遍性的論述，時態轉爲現在式如 seems, is, have，與之前幾句的過去時態完全不同。

1. ___百分比數據___ percent of all respondents agreed that ___應答者同意的事項___.

2. The majority of ___應答者___ (___百分比數據___%) also associated ___相關事項 A___ with ___相關事項 B___.

3. These ___應答者___ also expressed a strong desire for ___應答者表達強烈意願的事項___.

4. Almost ___百分比數據___% stated that they would like to ___應答者想要的事項 A___, and over half said that they would like to ___應答者想要的事項 B___.

5. It seems, then, that this group of ___應答者___ is ___對問卷結果的總結___.

練習

請按照以上講解說明以及你自己的研究內容，填入以下段落的空格來撰寫問卷調查的結果。

_____ percent of all respondents agreed that

_____. The majority of

_____ (_____%)

also associated _____ with

_____. These

_____ also expressed a strong desire for

_____. Almost

_____% stated that they would like to

_____, and over half said that they would like

to _____. It seems, then, that this group of

_____ is _____.

此範例是描述問卷的回收率，也是撰寫問卷調查結果的重要段落，重點在陳述回收問卷數量占總發出問卷數量的比例。而回收率較差的研究還要解釋原因，讓讀者了解並對問卷結果的詮釋比較保守。

① All of the above factors may have contributed to the fact that about a third of the questionnaires found their way back to us. ② However, such a return rate is not unusual in the social sciences, and is in fact rather high in comparison to other surveys in this research area. ③ Nevertheless, the fact that only 33.5 percent of the questionnaires were returned must be considered in thinking about the results, and those results must be interpreted cautiously.

以上因素可能導致我們只回收約三分之一的問卷，但是這樣的回收率在社會科學中很平常，事實上與相同研究領域的其他調查比較，此回收率還算高。不過只有收回 33.5% 的問卷就必須考量其結果，對這些結果的詮釋勢必要小心。

範例 2 講解

1　All of the above factors <u>may</u> <u>have contributed to</u> the fact that about <u>a third</u> of the questionnaires found their way back to us.

◎ 此句先解釋為何回收率如此低，並報告問卷回收率只有約三分之一，英文用 a third 或 one third 表示。英文分數的表達方式是將分子 (numerator) 和分母 (denominator) 分開對待，分子用基數如 one, two, three, four 等表示，而分母則是用序數如 third,

fourth, fifth 等表示。因此二分之一要寫成 one half、八分之一
要寫成 one eighth；而分子大於 1 時，分母要加複數 s，例如七
分之三要寫成 three sevenths，不能寫成 *three seventh。

○ 此句用 A have contributed to B 來表達「A 導致 B」的因果關
係，而助動詞 may 則可降低此因果關係論述的語氣，也是一種
「避險」。

2 <u>However</u>, such a return rate is not unusual in the social
sciences, and is in fact rather high <u>in comparison to</u> other
surveys in this research area.

○ 第 2 句說明此低回收率在該研究領域尚屬合理，句首先以表
「然而」的連接副詞 however 來做語氣的轉折，之後再提出和同
領域其他調查回收率的比較。

○ 表達「比較」用片語 in comparison to。

3 <u>Nevertheless</u>, the fact that only 33.5 percent of the
questionnaires were returned must be considered in
thinking about the results, and those results must be
interpreted cautiously.

○ 但回收率偏低畢竟不是好事，因此這句的句首再用一次表「然
而」的連接副詞 nevertheless，把語氣轉移回來，提醒讀者對於
研究結果的詮釋需多加小心。

範例 2　句型

1. All of the above factors may have contributed to the fact that about ___（問卷）回收率___ of the questionnaires found their way back to us.

2. However, such a return rate is not unusual in ___研究領域___, and is in fact rather high in comparison to other surveys in this research area.

3. Nevertheless, the fact that only ___回收率___ of the questionnaires were returned must be considered in thinking about the results, and those results must be interpreted cautiously.

練習

請按照以上講解說明以及你自己的研究內容，填入以下段落的空格來撰寫
問卷調查的回收率。

All of the above factors may have contributed to the fact that about

_____ of the questionnaires found

their way back to us. However, such a return rate is not unusual in

_____, and is in fact rather high in comparison

to other surveys in this research area. Nevertheless, the fact that only

_____ of the questionnaires were returned

must be considered in thinking about the results, and those results must

be interpreted cautiously.

範例 3

　　此範例是呈現兩組平均數 t 檢定的結果，一般需要報告平均數、標準差、t 檢定的 t 值以及 p 值是否具統計顯著性，而此例子還要看是否符合研究假設。

① An independent sample t test was conducted to evaluate the hypothesis that students talk more under a high-stress condition as opposed to a low-stress condition. ② The test was significant, t (28) = 2.43, p = .02, but the results were counter to the research hypothesis. ③ Students in the high-stress condition (M = 22.07, SD = 27.14) on the average talked less than those in the low-stress condition (M = 45.21, SD = 24.97). ④ Figure 2 shows the distribution of the two groups.

執行獨立樣本 t 檢定來評估此研究假設，亦即學生在高壓力環境中會比在低壓力環境下說更多話。**檢定結果具顯著性，t (28) = 2.43, p = .02**，但是此結果不符合假設。學生在高壓力環境下 **(M = 22.07, SD = 27.14)** 平均而言比在低壓力環境 **(M = 45.21, SD = 24.97)** 講的話要少。**圖 2 顯示這兩組的分配情況。**

範例 3 講解

1　An independent sample t test <u>was conducted</u> to evaluate the hypothesis that students talk more under a high-stress condition as opposed to a low-stress condition.

　　⊜ 首句指出使用獨立樣本 t 檢定的目的，是為了檢證此研究的假設。

◎ 動詞使用過去式被動語態 was conducted，而 conducted 也可以代換成 carried out, calculated, computed, performed 等。

◎ 有些作者習慣把 t 檢定用斜體字 t 或大寫 T 呈現。

2 The test was significant, t (28) = 2.43, p = .02, but the results were counter to the research hypothesis.

◎ 第 2 句寫 t 檢定的結果，除了具顯著性之外，還要記得報告自由度、t 值和 p 值是多少。另外，有的作者習慣把字母 t 和 p 用斜體字 t 和 p 呈現。

◎ 數據通常是寫到小數點後第二位。

3 Students in the high-stress condition (M = 22.07, SD = 27.14) on the average talked less than those in the low-stress condition (M = 45.21, SD = 24.97).

◎ 第 3 句比較兩組的差異，各自的平均數 (M) 和標準差 (SD) 可以寫在圓括號內來輔助文字說明。有些作者習慣把字母 M 和 SD 用斜體字 M 和 SD 呈現。

4 Figure 2 shows the distribution of the two groups.

◎ 最後一句要以圖表來呈現統計結果，動詞轉用現在式主動語態 shows，與前三句都用過去式不同。因為前三句都是在描述過去已經結束的統計結果，而這一句並沒有特定的時間點，只是告訴讀者圖表的位置，因此用現在式即可。

範例 3 句型

1. A(n) ___(t 檢定的）種類___ sample t test was conducted to evaluate
   the hypothesis that ___研究假設___ .

2. The test was significant, t (___自由度___) = ___t 值___ , p = ___p 值___ ,
   but the results were counter to the research hypothesis.

3. ___第一組研究對象的表現___ (M = ___M 值___ , SD = ___SD 值___)
   ___與第二組研究對象表現的比較___ (M = ___M 值___ , SD = ___SD 值___).

4. Figure ___（圖表）編號___ shows the distribution of the two groups.

練習

請按照以上講解說明以及你自己的研究內容，填入以下段落的空格來撰寫 t 檢定的結果。

A(n) _____ sample t test was conducted to

evaluate the hypothesis that _____.

The test was significant, t (_____) =

_____, p = _____,

but the results were counter to the research hypothesis.

_____ (M = _____,

SD = _____) _____

(M = _____,

SD = _____). Figure

_____ shows the distribution of the two

groups.

範例 4

　　撰寫相關性 (correlations) 分析的結果主要是要報告兩個變項間的關係 (relationship)，包括其方向 (direction) 是正向或負向相關，以及強度 (strength) 是高度或低度相關。此範例呈現三個相關性分析的結果，分別用 correlation, correlate, correlated 三個不同詞性的字所衍生的三個句型，頗具變化。寫作時也需要報告相關係數 r 值以及 p 值是否具統計顯著性。

① We found a significant correlation between students' summer 2008 TOEFL scores and GPA earned during fall 2008 ($r = .33$, $p < .05$). ② In addition, these TOEFL scores did correlate positively with the number of courses completed by the students ($r = .25$, $p < .05$), a finding consistent with Light's study (2007). ③ Finally, our analysis showed that these TOEFL scores were highly correlated with the total number of words written by the students in a writing sample administered at the same time ($r = .69$, $p < .0001$).

我們發現學生 2008 年夏季的托福分數與 2008 年秋季的在校平均成績 (GPA) 具顯著相關性 ($r = .33$, $p < .05$)。此外，這些托福分數與學生所修的課程數量有正相關 ($r = .25$, $p < .05$)，此結果與 Light (2007) 的研究一致。最後，我們的分析顯示這些托福分數與學生在同時期所寫的作文樣本總字數具有高度相關性 ($r = .69$, $p < .0001$)。

範例 4 講解

1

We found a significant correlation between students'
summer 2008 TOEFL scores and GPA earned during fall
2008 ($r = .33$, $p < .05$).

- 此句動詞時態用過去式 found。

- 相關性分析是描述兩個變項之間的關係，常用「a significant
correlation between 變項 A and 變項 B」的句型。而句末再用
圓括號來報告 r 值和 p 值。

2

In addition, these TOEFL scores did correlate positively
with the number of courses completed by the students ($r =$
$.25$, $p < .05$), a finding consistent with Light's study (2007).

- 句首用連接副詞 in addition（除此之外），告訴讀者這句呈現
第二個相關性分析的結果，也可以用 furthermore, moreover,
besides 代換。

- 在此句中，表達「相關」是用動詞 correlate，與第 1 句用名
詞 correlation 不同，因此句型也不一樣。這句是用「變項 A +
correlate positively with + 變項 B」，副詞 positively 表「正相
關」，如果是「負相關」，就改爲 negatively。接著再用圓括號來
報告 r 值和 p 值。

- 句子最後還與之前的研究結果作比較，常用 consistent with
表「一致」，也可以代換成 congruent with, compatible with,
in agreement with, in line with, in conformity with, in accord/
accordance with, in tune with 等。

3

Finally, our analysis showed that these TOEFL scores were highly correlated with the total number of words written by the students in a writing sample administered at the same time ($r = .69$, $p < .0001$).

- 最後一個相關性分析，句首用連接副詞 finally。
- 此句表達「相關」則是用形容詞 correlated，其前需要有 be 動詞，句型為「變項 A + be 動詞 + highly correlated with + 變項 B」，句尾再用圓括號來報告 r 值和 p 值。
- 句中 highly correlated 表「高度相關」，若要表達「中度相關」則可用 moderately correlated。
- 另外，correlated with 也可以代換成 associated with 或 related to。

範例 4　句型

1. We found a significant correlation between ___變項 A___ and ___變項 B___ ($r =$ ___r 值___, $p <$ ___p 值___).

2. In addition, ___變項 A___ did correlate positively with ___變項 B___ ($r =$ ___r 值___, $p <$ ___p 值___), a finding consistent with ___之前研究者___'s study (___出版年份___).

3. Finally, our analysis showed that ___變項 A___ were highly correlated with ___變項 B___ ($r =$ ___r 值___, $p <$ ___p 值___).

練習

請按照以上講解說明以及你自己的研究內容，填入以下段落的空格來撰寫相關性分析的結果。

We found a significant correlation between

_____ and _____

(r = _____ ,

p < _____). In addition,

_____ did correlate positively with

_____ (r = _____ ,

p < _____),

a finding consistent with _____ 's study

(_____). Finally, our analysis showed

that _____ were highly correlated with

_____ (r = _____ ,

p < _____).

此範例是針對某一教師的質性個案研究，陳述資料分析完後所得到的分類範疇。在寫作時可先說明分析出幾個範疇，之後再一一討論每個範疇的特性，以及引述研究對象所說的話來支持研究者的論述。質性研究的結果通常篇幅相當多，也不容易歸納出常用的句型架構。因此以下範例就省略大部分的內容字，只留下架構。

① In analyzing the data, three knowledge categories emerged: (a) classroom organization and operation, (b) teaching behavior, and (c) external conditions. ② Each category was unique in terms of the problems it addressed and the source from which it came.

③ Classroom Organization and Operation
④ Like many teachers (West, 1995; Liao, 2006), classroom order and control were predominant concerns for Bob. ⑤ The concern for classroom organization and controlled operation rose from Bob's belief that, if order was not established and the classroom not operated in the manner he needed, little could be accomplished. ⑥ In his own words,

......

分析完資料後，三種知識**範疇浮現出來**：(a) 教室組織與運作，(b) 教學行為，(c) 外在條件。**每種範疇就其**討論的問題和問題的來源**而言都很獨特**。

教室組織與運作
如同許多教師一般 (West, 1995; Liao, 2006)，Bob 也覺得教室秩序和控制是最重要的事。對於教室組織和控制運作的關切源自於 Bob 的信念，他相信如果沒有建立秩序，而且教室未在他需要的情況下運作，課堂教學成效就會低落。**他說道：**

......

範例5 講解

1 In analyzing the data, three knowledge categories emerged: (a) classroom organization and operation, (b) teaching behavior, and (c) external conditions.

- 第 1 句先寫分析完資料後所得的結果，也就是有三個範疇。

- 質性研究對於資料分析的結果常用動詞 emerge（浮現），凸顯資料本身是在自然的情況下生成出現，不像量性研究的結果常是透過變項的操控和人為介入才能取得。

- 陳述範疇時是以一系列三個項目 (a) (b) (c) 的方式呈現，必須以逗號將各個範疇隔開，而且在最後一個範疇 (c) 之前通常會加連接詞 and 和逗號。但有些作者習慣在最後一個項目前不加連接詞，形成 (a) classroom organization and operation, (b) teaching behavior, (c) external conditions，這樣也可以。

2 Each category was unique in terms of the problems it addressed and the source from which it came.

- 第 2 句繼續說明範疇的特性，句首用形容詞 each 修飾主詞 category，因此動詞要用單數 was 才能與主詞一致。

3 Classroom Organization and Operation

- 接下來要分段講述每個範疇，不過 Classroom Organization and Operation 並不是句子，而是第一個範疇的標題。

4 Like many teachers (West, 1995; Liao, 2006), classroom order and control were predominant concerns for Bob.

- 第 4 句開始闡述第一個範疇，並與之前的研究文獻作比較。

5 The concern for classroom organization and controlled operation rose from Bob's belief <u>that</u>, <u>if</u> order was not established and the classroom not operated in the manner he needed, little could be accomplished.

○ 第 5 句繼續闡述第一個範疇的細節，此句相當長，可注意 that 後面插入一個從屬連接詞 if 所引導的子句，子句間要加逗號，閱讀起來比較清楚。

6 In his own words,
......

○ 最後直接引述研究對象所說的話，記得 word 要加 s。在質性分析的結果中引述受訪者的話是非常重要的，不能都是由研究者詮釋受訪者的文字，必須時常由研究對象自己發出聲音，才能提高分析結果的信度。而在引介出研究對象的受訪內容時，可以參考以下的常用句型：

• For example, one interviewee remarked/said,
  例如一位受訪者評論 / 說道：

• As one student commented/said,
  如一名學生評論 / 說道：

• The following comment can help enlighten us on this.
  以下評論有助於我們了解這件事：

• The following was a typical comment made by the respondents.
  以下是受訪者的典型評論：

• The following comment made by one of the informants was probably the most typical.
  以下這位受訪者所說的可能是最典型的評論：

209

• The following remarks made by two of the respondents were obviously pertinent.

由兩位受訪者提供明顯相關的評論如下：

範例 5 句型

1. In analyzing the data, ___幾個（範疇）___ categories emerged:
   (a) ___第一個範疇___ , (b) ___第二個範疇___ , and (c) ___第三個範疇___ .

2. Each category was unique in terms of ___範疇的特性___ .

3. ___第一個範疇的標題___

4. ___闡述第一個範疇___ .

5. ___繼續闡述第一個範疇___ .

6. In his own words,

   ___直接引述受訪者的話___ .

練習

請按照以上講解說明以及你自己的研究內容，填入以下段落的空格來撰寫質性分析的結果。

In analyzing the data, _____ categories

emerged: (a) _____,

(b)_____, and (c)

_____. Each category was unique in terms of

_____.

_____

_____. _____.

In his own words, _____.

Graphics and Locations of Results
圖表與研究結果所在

用圖表呈現研究結果可以濃縮複雜的資料使人一目了然，提高讀者的閱讀效率。但不能為了達到所謂「看起來比較專業」而濫用圖表，原本用文字能說明清楚的內容就不需要附上圖表來增加篇幅。也有人一旦附上圖表就忘了還需要配合文字說明，反而讓讀者看得很辛苦，就達不到原來一目了然的效果。因此記得文字和圖表要相互搭配，圖表可有效呈現複雜的概念和數據，而文字則要說明這些概念數據的意義。

圖表一般可分為圖 (graph, diagram, chart) 和表 (table)，在文中替圖表編號時一般是用阿拉伯數字如 Table 1，而不用羅馬數字如 Figure II 或英文字母如 Figure C 等。可能的例外是在附錄 (Appendices) 中的圖表編號，例如附錄 B 的第三個表，就可編碼成 Table B-3。另外，寫作時還常需要用文字指出圖表的所在位置，此時的時態就只能用現在式，而語態則是主動被動都可以。

範例 1

此範例是分析完問卷後用圖表呈現結果的陳述，而說明圖表所在位置的寫法基本上有兩種，一種是寫在句子中；另一種則是當作附加資訊寫在圓括號中。此範例就使用了這兩種寫法。

① For all items in Questions 1-4, the Wilcoxon test showed statistically significant differences. ② These results are summarized in Tables 1 and 2. ③ Further, the differences in responses to Questions 10 and 11 were also statistically significant (see Table 3 below).

問卷第 1-4 題用 Wilcoxon 檢定，顯示具有統計上的顯著差異，這些結果總結在表 1 和表 2。另外，對於第 10 題和第 11 題的回應也有統計上的顯著性（見以下的表 3）。

範例 1 **講解**

1 For all items in Questions 1-4, the Wilcoxon test <u>showed</u> <u>statistically significant differences</u>.

- 首句寫問卷分析的題數和統計檢定的結果，因為統計分析在過去已經結束，因此時態用過去式 showed。

- 表達「統計上的顯著差異」的詞組是用副詞 statistically 修飾形容詞 significant 再修飾名詞 differences 所形成。

2 These results <u>are summarized</u> in Tables 1 and 2.

- 此句指出統計結果用表格呈現的位置，而凡是要表達文中圖表所在的時態一律都用現在式，而且主動或被動語態皆可，因此本句用現在式被動語態 are summarized。如果要改成主動語態就變成以下句子：

  • Tables 1 and 2 summarize these results.

3 <u>Further</u>, the differences in responses to Questions 10 and 11 were also statistically significant (<u>see</u> Table 3 below).

- 因為除了第 1 句和第 2 句之外還有其他統計結果，因此本句開頭先用連接副詞 further 表「再者；另外」。

- 此句把圖表資訊置於句尾的圓括號中，當作附屬資訊，加上動詞 see 會比較清楚。

範例1 **句型**

1. For all items in Questions ____(問卷)題數____, ____統計檢定的方法____
showed statistically significant differences.

2. These results are summarized in Tables ____(表格)編號____ and ____(表
格)編號____.

3. Further, the differences in responses to Questions ____題數____ were
also statistically significant (see Table ____編號____ below).

練習

請按照以上講解說明以及你自己的研究內容，填入以下段落的空格來說明圖表位置。

For all items in Questions _____,

_____ showed statistically

significant differences. These results are summarized in Tables

_____ and _____.

Further, the differences in responses to Questions

_____ were also statistically significant (see

Table _____ below).

範例 2

此範例呈現描述性統計和 F 檢定結果所在的圖表。

---

① Table 3 presents the means and standard deviations for level of depression by treatment group and race. ② The mean differences in these tables are quite small, varying by only one or two points from the grand mean of 17.1 ($N = 488$, $SD = 9.9$). ③ As shown in Table 6, there were no statistically significant main or interaction effects: $F (1, 478) = .84$, $p = .36$.

表三呈現處理組中族裔的沮喪程度之平均數和標準差。在這些表格中平均數的差異都相當小，與總平均數 17.1 (**N** = 488, **SD** = 9.9) 都只差一兩分。如表 6 所示，主要和互動效果都不具統計顯著性，**F** (1, 478) = .84, **p** = .36。

範例2 **講解**

1 | Table 3 <u>presents</u> the means and standard deviations for level of depression by treatment group and race.

⊖ 此句先寫描述性統計的主題，主詞用 table，接現在式主動語態動詞 presents，此動詞也可代換成 shows, indicates, displays, demonstrates, illustrates, reveals, summarizes, lists, contains 等。

2 | The mean differences in these tables are quite small, <u>varying by</u> only one or two points from the grand mean of 17.1 ($N = 488$, $SD = 9.9$).

- 此句寫各組平均數以及它們與總平均數的差異，而差異的大小用逗號之後的現在分詞片語 varying by... 來表示。
- 最後可用圓括號中的斜體字寫出個數 (*N*) 和標準差 (*SD*) 是多少。

3 <u>As shown in</u> Table 6, there were no statistically significant main or interaction effects: F (1, 478) = .84, p = .36.

- 最後一句寫變異數分析 (ANOVA) 之 F 檢定的結果，除了是否具統計顯著性之外，還必須寫出 F 值和 p 值，可用斜體字寫成 *F* 和 *p*。
- 句首「as shown in + 圖表」是常用句型，as 之後一定要加過去分詞如 shown, indicated, displayed, demonstrated, illustrated, revealed, summarized, listed, contained, presented 等，而介系詞絕大部分都是用 in 再接圖表。

範例 2 句型

1. Table ___編號___ presents the means and standard deviations for ___受測組別___.

2. The mean differences in these tables are ___（平均數的）差異___, varying by ___個別平均數與總平均數的差異___ (*N* = ___N 值___, *SD* = ___SD 值___).

3. As shown in Table ___編號___, there were no statistically significant main or interaction effects: F (___自由度___) = ___F 值___, p = ___p 值___.

練習

請按照以上講解說明以及你自己的研究內容，填入以下段落的空格來說明
圖表位置。

Table _____ presents the means and standard

deviations for _____. The mean differences

in these tables are _____, varying by

_____ (*N* = _____,

SD = _____). As shown in Table

_____, there were no statistically significant

main or interaction effects: *F* (_____) =

_____, *p* = _____.

Discussion and Conclusions
討論 / 結論

Discussion and Conclusions

　　論文最後一章討論／結論是針對研究結果這一章提出研究者個人的詮釋，並將個別研究結果聯結至整個研究領域作整合。但是有些人只是換個方式再重述整個研究，並沒有達到討論的要求。所謂討論應該達到以下功能：

(1) 解釋研究結果的意義，看是否能驗證在緒論中提出的假設或達到研究目的。

(2) 比較自己與之前相關的研究結果，看有何相同或相異之處。

(3) 提出研究的理論義涵或實務應用，看能對整個領域做出何種貢獻。

(4) 最後再承認自己研究的限制並建議未來的研究，看指出了什麼新的研究主題或方向。

　　討論的寫作鋪陳恰好與緒論相反，緒論的行文順序是從普遍至特定 (from general to specific)，而討論則是顛倒過來從特定至普遍 (from specific to general)，也就是先寫本研究的結論、探討研究結果，再逐漸擴大寫本研究對整個研究領域的義涵和應用。具體來說，討論一章可以區分為以下四個小節：

1. Conclusions（研究結論）

2. Review of Research Findings（探討研究發現）

3. Limitations of the Study（研究限制）

4. Suggestions for Future Research（建議未來研究）

以上四小節中又以第二節的「探討研究發現」最為重要，內容通常還會包括解釋研究結果、與之前研究作比較、說明研究的義涵和應用等，篇幅最多也最難寫。當然不同學科領域對於討論的寫作還是有不同的要求，有所謂的學科變異性 (disciplinary variation)，寫作者最好還是遵循自己研究領域的期刊論文所做的規定和小節標題的慣用表達方式。不過以下的範例仍能提供許多寫作上的參考架構。

Conclusions
研究結論

研究結論是對整篇論文做一總結性的回顧陳述，包括概述前一章的主要研究結果，並簡要地提出此研究的義涵或應用，為以下更詳盡的討論作準備。但不宜提出之前從未出現過的新議題或結果，或只是重述抄錄之前章節中相同的句子。

範例

以下結論的範例先寫出研究的主題，再接著寫研究的主要發現，這些都是之前章節中的資訊，在此先做回顧性的概述。第 3 句之後就開始寫研究義涵，接著是解釋結果和建議未來研究，這些都只是簡要的描述，為之後更詳實的討論作準備。

① To conclude, the present study is preliminary research on time use and pause patterns in translation and text production, but its relevance to segmentation research can also be seen. ② A major finding is that the effect of translation can be observed in pause lengths at all linguistic levels of the writing process. ③ The results indicate that translation is a slower activity than text production at word and clause levels. ④ It can be reasoned that translation requires more time for word choice and clause formation. ⑤ But it remains unclear why translation should slow down the actual writing of words.

總結而言，本研究是對於翻譯和寫作的時間使用與停頓模式之初步研究，但也與分節研究相關。研究主要發現在書寫過程中，每個語文層次都可觀察到翻譯所

造成的停頓。**這些結果指出**在字彙和子句層次上，翻譯都比寫作還要慢。**這可推論出**翻譯需要更多的時間來選擇字彙和造句，**但仍不清楚的是**為何翻譯會減緩實際寫字的速度。

範例 講解

1
<u>To conclude</u>, the present study is preliminary research <u>on</u> time use and pause patterns in translation and text production, <u>but</u> its relevance to segmentation research can also be seen.

- 句首用 to conclude 很明確告訴讀者該段要做此文的結論，也可寫成 in conclusion, in sum, to summarize 等。
- 接下來在介系詞 on 之後寫此研究的主題。
- 在兩個子句間用表「對反」的對等連接詞 but，表示此研究與其他主題也有關聯 (relevance)，也算是本研究的另一種貢獻。

2
A <u>major finding</u> is that the effect of translation can be observed in pause lengths at all linguistic levels of the writing process.

- 第 1 句寫了研究主題後，第 2 句繼續描述研究的主要發現，除了用 major 修飾 finding 外，也可用 main, primary, substantial, critical, chief, key 等字。

Discussion and Conclusions

3 The results <u>indicate</u> that translation is a slower activity than text production at word and clause levels.

◌ 從上句的主要發現再往下發展，第 3 句寫具體的研究義涵，動詞用 indicate。

4 It can <u>be reasoned</u> that translation requires more time for word choice and clause formation.

◌ 此句是對上句的研究結果提出解釋，動詞用被動語態的 be reasoned。

5 <u>But</u> it <u>remains</u> <u>unclear</u> why translation should slow down the actual writing of words.

◌ 最後再寫此研究尚未探討清楚的地方，可以作為未來研究的可能性。

◌ 用連接詞 but 開頭是要表達與前幾句文意相反的轉折。

◌ remain 是不及物動詞，其後接形容詞 unclear，而 unclear 也可代換成 unresolved 或 undefined 等。

1. To conclude, the present study is preliminary research on ___此研究的主題___, but its relevance to ___其他研究主題___ can also be seen.

2. A major finding is that ___本研究主要發現___.

3. The results indicate that ___本研究義涵___.

4. It can be reasoned that ___解釋上述研究發現___.

5. But it remains unclear why ___本研究尚未探討清楚之處___.

練習

請按照以上講解說明以及你自己的研究內容，填入以下段落的空格來撰寫研究結論。

To conclude, the present study is preliminary research

on _____, but its relevance to

_____ can also be seen. A major finding

is that _____. The results indicate

that _____. It can be reasoned that

_____. But it remains unclear why

_____.

Review of Research Findings
探討研究發現

　　探討研究發現是討論這一章的重心，事實上也是整個研究的價值所在。前一章雖然已經提出了研究結果，但這些成果對讀者具有什麼意義，如何去理解和運用這些結果，就要靠此節來闡釋說明。基本上此節對研究結果要從各種層面作分析解釋，並與同領域其他研究結果比較，再提出自己的研究對整個領域的義涵和實用價值。因此在撰寫此節時可再分為以下三個部分：

　　(1) Giving a Possible Explanation for the Results
　　　　解釋研究的結果
　　(2) Comparing Your Results with Those of Other Studies
　　　　與其他研究作比較
　　(3) Suggesting Implications/Applications of the Study
　　　　說明研究的義涵 / 應用

以下分述之。

1 Giving a Possible Explanation for the Results
解釋研究的結果

　　雖然作者需要對其研究做出解釋，但畢竟解釋也是作者個人主觀的詮解，對於事物背後的抽象本質或因果關係並不是我們有限的感官經驗可以完全掌握，因此在做解釋時的論述仍要保守謹慎，也就是所謂的「避險」。避險的機制可以使用表可能性的助動詞如 may, might, could, would 等字；表可能性的副詞如 probably, possibly, perhaps, apparently；表可能性的形容詞如 possible, probable, likely 等字；表建議和推測性的動詞如 suggest, propose, seem, appear, believe, speculate 等字。更要避免使用全稱或絕對性的論述如 always, never 或 Everyone knows that... 等。

我們也可以用中文論文寫作的句子來做一個對照，例如有同學的論文寫道：「此結果**證明**翻譯試題**確實**是以老師方便閱卷爲命題方向。」這就是百分之百肯定的論述，但因果關係的事實是否眞的如此是沒有人確切知道的，因此容易引起別人的質疑和挑戰。如果用避險的機制可寫成：「此結果**顯示**翻譯試題**似乎**是以老師方便閱卷爲命題方向。」就比較不會有過度歸因的問題。再看一例：「非選擇題表現優良的學生，其選擇題部分**必定**也能答得得心應手。」最好改成「非選擇題表現優良的學生，其選擇題部分**通常**也能答得得心應手。」才能降低作者主張或宣稱事實的強度，而英文論文寫作的「避險」機制也是如此。

範例

此範例要解釋研究的結果，尤其是此研究的統計分析結果並未達到顯著性，作者更需加以解釋。

---

① One possible reason for there being no statistical significance may lie in the small size of the non-CALL group. ② In the present study, only 27 college teachers did not adopt CALL into their language teaching. ③ Moreover, another possible reason may be that teachers' age, educational background, and years of teaching experience actually have little to do with their teaching decision-making. ④ To people's common impression, younger or junior teachers may be more open-minded toward innovative technology; however, the findings here could provide some empirical evidence to clarify the myth.

統計結果未達顯著性的可能原因在於非電腦輔助語言教學 (non-CALL) 組的人數過少。在本研究中，只有 27 位大學教師沒有使用電腦輔助語言教學。而且另一可能原因是教師的年齡、教育背景和教學年資事實上都與他們的教學決策沒有太大關係。一般人的印象好像年輕和新進教師對創新科技可能採比較開放的態度，但是本研究的發現可提供實徵證據來打破此迷思。

範例 **講解**

1 One possible reason for there being no statistical significance may lie in the small size of the non-CALL group.

- 首句先指出沒有達到統計顯著性的第一個理由，但因為要避險，作者用形容詞 possible 來修飾 reason，還用助動詞 may 表可能性。

- 句首 one possible reason 也可代換成 a possible explanation 或 a plausible interpretation。

- 動詞 lie in 與「說謊」無關，而是指「在於…」。

- 與這句解釋研究結果類似的句型還有：

  - A partial explanation for this result may lie in the fact that...
    對此結果的部分解釋為……

  - A possible explanation for this is that...
    此結果的可能解釋為……

  - Such an explanation may account for...
    這個解釋可說明……

  - This is likely due to...
    這可能是因為……

或用被動語態，如下句：

• These results may be explained by...
這些結果可以……來解釋。

2 In the present study, only 27 college teachers did not adopt CALL into their language teaching.

◎ 第 2 句繼續解釋沒有統計顯著性的原因，回到研究本身來探討，時態必須用過去式。

3 Moreover, another possible reason may be that teachers' age, educational background, and years of teaching experience actually have little to do with their teaching decision-making.

◎ 句首連接副詞 moreover 提示讀者以下還有第二個解釋的理由。

◎ 避險機制和第 1 句一樣使用 possible 和 may。

◎ 要表達「A 與 B 沒有太大關係」時，可以用 A have little to do with B。

4 To people's common impression, younger or junior teachers may be more open-minded toward innovative technology; however, the findings here could provide some empirical evidence to clarify the myth.

◎ 最後一句是反過來將未達到統計顯著性視為正面的研究結果，也就是可打破一般人對年輕新進教師的迷思。

◎ 兩個句子間用連接副詞 however，特別要注意其標點符號用法，
however 之前用分號，之後用逗號。

◎ 最後一句也有避險，使用助動詞 could。

1. One possible reason for there being no statistical significance may
lie in _____解釋研究結果不具統計顯著性的第一個原因_____.

2. In the present study, _____回到研究本身來解釋結果_____.

3. Moreover, another possible reason may be that _____第二個解釋研究結果
的原因_____.

4. _____與研究結果不符預期的迷思_____; however, the findings here could
provide some empirical evidence to clarify the myth.

練習

請按照以上講解說明以及你自己的研究內容，填入以下段落的空格來解釋
研究結果。

One possible reason for there being no statistical significance

may lie in _____. In the present study,

_____. Moreover, another possible reason

may be that _____.

_____; however, the findings here could

provide some empirical evidence to clarify the myth.

Comparing Your Results with Those of Other Studies
與其他研究作比較

　　將自己研究的結果與同領域其他研究結果作比較，也是撰寫討論一
章中很重要的一部分，透過比較才能明確指出自己的研究在整個領域的
定位和價值。研究領域可以視為一幅拼圖，每個研究都只是其中一小塊
圖，而自己研究的這塊圖要如何與其他研究者的圖拼湊在一起，就是要
作研究結果的比較才知道。有相符的圖可拼在一起，不一致的圖就再繼
續與其他研究比較，最後才能整合或擴大研究領域的全幅面貌。

　　而且作研究結果比較時，應該是就緒論一章文獻回顧時所探討過的
研究來和自己目前的研究作比較，才有前後呼應的合理性。此時不宜突
然提出新的研究文獻來比較，那等於承認之前文獻探討的研究與你目前
的研究沒有直接關係，減損文獻探討的價值。另外要注意的是，在撰寫
研究比較時大多是用現在式。

範例

　　此段範例撰寫與其他研究結果的比較，比較的結果不外乎是一
致、不同或部分相同，此範例涵蓋這三種情況，另外還提到研究結果的
義涵。

① Our findings are not in contradiction with those of the empirical
studies discussed above. ② With regard to free recall with articulatory
suppression, our findings confirm those of Padilla (1995), although
there are important differences regarding other aspects of the studies.
③ These results lend some credence to the hypothesis that simultaneous
interpreting between two languages generates phonological

interference (e.g. Isham & Lane, 1994). ④ The better performance under articulatory suppression seems to be indicative of the fact that the practice of the simultaneous-interpreting task leads to greater resistance to phonological interference. ⑤ This finding also suggests that simultaneous interpreters do not rely on phonological rehearsal. ⑥ However, our data suggest that it is not exactly the degree of expertise in the interpreting task which leads to greater resistance to interference in the articulatory suppression condition, since the highest scores were not obtained by the expert group but by the novice group—contrary to Padilla's findings.

我們的發現並未抵觸之前討論過的實徵研究結果。在發音抑制的自由回想上,我們的發現證實了 Padilla (1995) 的研究結果,可是在研究的其他層面上仍有明顯差異。這些結果某種程度上可支持兩種語言同步口譯會產生語音干擾的假設(例如 Isham & Lane, 1994)。在發音抑制下的表現愈好,似乎顯示出從事同步口譯工作更能防制語音的干擾。此發現也指出同步口譯員並未依賴語音複述。然而我們的資料顯示,在發音抑制的情況下,口譯工作的專業程度對防制干擾的幫助不大,因為得分最高的組別並不是專家口譯員,而是新進譯者——此結果與 Padilla 的發現正好相反。

1 Our <u>findings</u> are <u>not in contradiction with</u> <u>those</u> of the empirical studies discussed above.

○ 第 1 句先指出此研究的結果與之前文獻探討過的研究沒有矛盾，用 not in contradiction with 表示，這是相對較為保守的寫法，其實就是說與之前的研究結果也沒有完全一致，只能說是接近一致。如果要表達較高的「一致性」則可用 consistent with, congruent with, compatible with, in agreement with, in line with, in conformity with, in accord/accordance with, in tune with 等片語。

○ 研究結果比較的基礎要相同，句中 our findings 是與 those of the empirical studies 比較，而 those 就是之前 findings 的代名詞，等於是 findings of the empirical studies；而如果之前的名詞是單數 finding，那麼代名詞就要用 that，這樣才是合理的比較。但是台灣的同學受到中文思考影響常會漏加代名詞，而誤寫為以下句子：

• *Our findings are not in contradiction with the empirical studies discussed above.

這樣的句子如果用中文的意義思考好像還蠻正確的，但就變成是 findings 與 studies 兩個不同的東西在比較，不符合英文語法，需多加小心。

2 <u>With regard to</u> free recall with articulatory suppression, our <u>findings</u> confirm <u>those</u> of Padilla (1995), <u>although</u> there are important differences <u>regarding</u> other aspects of the studies.

○ 第 1 句是比較目前和之前研究結果的一般性陳述 (general statement)，而第 2 句接下來就是針對特定的例子 (specific example) 來說明。

◎ 寫作上常用 with regard to 表「有關於…」，其中 to 是介系詞，其意等同於 in regard to, regarding, as regards，而 as regards 一定要在 regard 之後加 s；第二個子句中的 regarding 本身是介系詞，之後不能加 to，用法等於 concerning。

◎ 此句中的 those 是代替 findings，所以 those of Padilla (1995) 意指 Padilla 於 1995 年發表的研究結果。

◎ 本文旨在強調並非所有的研究結果都相符，因此從屬連接詞 although 後接的子句就告訴讀者還有其他研究層面是不同的，也就是說雖然目前的研究結果可以證實之前 Padilla 在 1995 年研究的某些結論，但也有許多地方不同。

3 These results <u>lend some credence to</u> the hypothesis that simultaneous interpreting between two languages generates phonological interference (<u>e.g.</u> Isham & Lane, 1994).

◎ 第 3 句寫目前研究結果的理論義涵，亦即在某種程度上支持該假設是可信的，用 lend some credence to 表示，其中動詞 lend 也可以代換成 give。

◎ 此假設在之前研究文獻中已經提過，因此作者在句尾用圓括號補充文獻資訊。e.g. 是拉丁文，也就是英文的 for example（舉例），有些人會在 e.g. 後再加逗號，形成 e.g.,，也可以。

4 The better performance under articulatory suppression seems to <u>be indicative of</u> the fact that the practice of the simultaneous-interpreting task leads to greater resistance to phonological interference.

◎ 此句承接上面句意繼續寫研究結果的義涵，句中 be indicative of 是相當正式的寫法，表「顯示出」。

◎ 其後 the fact that 之後要接一個子句。

5 This finding also <u>suggests</u> that simultaneous interpreters do not rely on phonological rehearsal.

- 此句繼續寫研究結果的另一個義涵，動詞 suggest 表示並不是百分之百肯定，但已經足以表達作者的主張，在論文寫作中極為常用。

6 <u>However,</u> our data suggest that it is not exactly the degree of expertise in the interpreting task which leads to greater resistance to interference in the articulatory suppression condition, <u>since</u> the highest scores were not obtained by the expert group but by the novice group—<u>contrary to</u> Padilla's findings.

- 前幾句都在寫與之前研究結果大致相符之處，但最後一句則是反過來表述此次研究結果與之前研究結果不同的層面，來呼應第 2 句 although 之後的子句，這樣的比較才較為客觀全面。

- 句首先用表「然而」的連接副詞 however，再寫出自己研究的不同義涵，並以表「因果關係」的連接詞 since 引導的子句來解釋不同的原因，最後才用破折號 (dash) 補充說明此結果與 Padilla 的研究結果相反。此處用副詞片語 contrary to 表達「相反」，不能用 contrary of。

1. Our findings are not in contradiction with those of the empirical studies discussed above.

2. With regard to ＿＿研究結果的某一層面＿＿, our findings confirm those of ＿＿之前的研究者＿＿, although there are important differences regarding other aspects of the studies.

3. These results lend some credence to the hypothesis that ＿＿目前研究所支持的假設＿＿ (e.g. ＿＿之前的研究文獻＿＿).

4. ＿＿目前研究的結果＿＿ seems to be indicative of the fact that ＿＿研究結果的義涵 A＿＿.

5. This finding also suggests that ＿＿研究結果的義涵 B＿＿.

6. However, our data suggest that ＿＿與之前研究結果不同的義涵＿＿, since ＿＿與之前研究結果不同的原因＿＿—contrary to ＿＿之前研究者的＿＿ findings.

練習

請按照以上講解說明以及你自己的研究內容，填入以下段落的空格來比較其他的研究。

Our findings are not in contradiction with those of the empirical studies

discussed above. With regard to _____,

our findings confirm those of _____,

although there are important differences regarding other aspects of

the studies. These results lend some credence to the hypothesis that

_____ (e.g. _____).

_____ seems to be indicative of the fact that

_____. This finding also suggests that

_____. However, our data suggest that

_____, since _____

—contrary to _____ findings.

3 Suggesting Implications/Applications of the Study
說明研究的義涵／應用

　　論文接近尾聲時就應該要提出該研究的理論義涵 (theoretical implications) 或實務應用 (practical applications)，作為對整個研究的總結，同時也凸顯其貢獻和意義，並和緒論一章撰寫的「研究價值」相互呼應，看看是否已達成原先預期的價值。

　　個別研究的結果是特定的，而研究的義涵或應用是比較具有普遍性的，也就是說從個別的研究結果要能向外擴充影響至整個研究領域，這樣的研究才有價值意義。而理論義涵通常強調該研究結果如何外推 (generalize) 或轉移 (transfer) 到類似的情境，可以描述、解釋或預測更廣泛的現象或事件。而實務應用則偏重在研究結果如何解決或改善此研究情境以外的實際問題或困難。

　　但是寫研究義涵或應用時不能只是提供一些常識性的說法，例如有些人做教室個案研究，卻動不動就要教育行政當局負責解決問題，顯得有些空泛而不切實際。應該從研究的成果出發，緊扣所得的結論來提出對相關領域有意義的理論義涵或實務應用。

範例 1

　　以下範例偏向撰寫理論上的義涵，論述國際間的學者撰寫學術論文時如何受到西方學術訓練的影響。因為研究義涵的內容較為深入繁複，常分為好幾個段落，以下範例省略論述的過程，只保留主要架構，方便讀者了解學習。

---

① The present findings contribute to the field's understanding of the various forces acting on **TESOL** professionals as they prepare manuscripts for scholarly publication. ② One such force is the impact of Western training. ③ Kachru (1995) urges TESOL professionals to appreciate L1 rhetorical styles that represent the multiple voices of international writers of English; however, the 14 nonnative-English speaking TESOL scholars in this study tended to write their L1 academic papers in the conventionally accepted, Anglo-American manner. ...

④ A related issue concerns the choice of conventions for academic writing. ...

⑤ The present findings also confirm previous evidence that dominant Western academic traditions moderate local expository values in several countries (Purves, 2002).

⑥ Future research should investigate how English writing conventions nativize in L1 writing. ⑦ Finally, the study suggests that mainland Chinese TESOL scholars publish most of their studies in Chinese journals. ⑧ This is in contrast to academics in Hong Kong, who publish only their less significant work in Chinese journals (Flowerdew, 1999). ...

本研究發現有助研究領域了解英語教學 (TESOL) 專家在撰寫學術論文時**所受到的各種影響**。**其中一種影響就是**西方的學術訓練。Kachru (1995) **極力主張**英語教學專家要能欣賞第一語言的修辭風格，它們代表了國際間英文寫作者的多元聲音；**然而**，本研究中的 14 位母語非英語的英語教學學者，卻傾向在其第一語言的學術論文中使用英美慣用的方式。……

另一相關的議題為學術寫作上慣例的選擇。……

本研究結果也證實之前的研究證據，指出優勢的西方學術傳統在其他國家中會降低當地論述方式的地位 (Purves, 2002)。

未來的研究應該探討英文寫作慣例如何在第一語言寫作中本土化。最後，本研究指出中國大陸的英語教學學者將大部分的研究發表在中文期刊。此結果與香港學者成對比，香港學者只將較不重要的研究發表在中文期刊上 (Flowerdew, 1999)。……

範例 1　講解

1　The present findings <u>contribute to</u> the field's understanding of the various <u>forces</u> acting on TESOL professionals as they prepare manuscripts for scholarly publication.

- 第 1 句寫本研究對整個研究領域的貢獻，亦即了解各種「影響力」(forces)。
- 句中的動詞 contribute to 在語意正面的情況下有「貢獻；有助於」之意，但在負面語意時則表示「導致」，例如下句：

- Broken homes and undesirable community influences may be the factors that contribute to maladjustment among children.
  破碎的家庭和不良社區影響都可能是**導致**兒童適應不佳的因素。

2　One such <u>force</u> is the impact of Western training.

- 第 2 句進一步說明第 1 句所說的 force 是什麼。

3 Kachru (1995) <u>urges</u> TESOL professionals to appreciate L1 rhetorical styles that represent the multiple voices of international writers of English<u>; however,</u> the 14 nonnative-English speaking TESOL scholars in this study tended to write their L1 academic papers in the conventionally accepted, Anglo-American manner.

- 此句承接上句所說的西方訓練影響,並引用學者意見來作比較。
- 這句其實有兩個句子,中間用分號和連接副詞 however 隔開,顯示兩句的句意對反且關係緊密。
- Kachru (1995) 之後的動詞 urge 是比 suggest, indicate, say 等更強烈的用法,表「極力主張」。

4 A related issue <u>concerns</u> the choice of conventions for academic writing.

- 第 4 句是另立一段來寫研究的相關義涵,動詞時態用現在式 concerns。

5 The present findings also <u>confirm previous evidence that</u> dominant Western academic traditions moderate local expository values in several countries (Purves, 2002).

- 第 5 句又另立一段,主要是用來與之前的研究作比較,因此 confirm previous evidence 後面用 that 引導的形容詞子句修飾先行詞 evidence。
- 句末再用資訊顯著的引用方式將作者和出版年份置於圓括號內。

6 <u>Future research</u> should investigate how English writing conventions nativize in L1 writing.

　　◎ 基於前文的內容，此句建議未來可做的研究，future research 也可代換成 further research。

7 <u>Finally</u>, the study <u>suggests that</u> mainland Chinese TESOL scholars publish most of their studies in Chinese journals.

　　◎ 句首 finally 指出這已是最後一個研究義涵，動詞常用 suggest，而之後加 that 子句。

8 This <u>is in contrast to</u> academics in Hong Kong, who publish only their less significant work in Chinese journals (Flowerdew, 1999).

　　◎ 最後一個研究義涵與之前的文獻結果有出入，因此在提供資訊顯著引用之後，以下的內容就針對兩個研究的差異作說明。

　　◎ 要表達「A 與 B 成對比」時，可用「A + be 動詞 + in contrast to + B」。

1. The present findings contribute to the field's understanding of the various forces acting on ___對研究領域的影響___ .

2. One such force is ___其中一種影響力___ .

3. ___文獻中的研究者___ urges ___該研究者強烈主張的事項___ ; however, ___與之前研究者對反的觀點或事實___ .

4. A related issue concerns ___本研究另一研究義涵___ .

5. The present findings also confirm previous evidence that ___本研究證實之前研究之處___ .

6. Future research should investigate ___對未來研究的建議___ .

7. Finally, the study suggests that ___本研究最後一個研究義涵___ .

8. This is in contrast to ___本研究義涵與之前研究文獻不同之處___ .

練習

請按照以上講解說明以及你自己的研究內容，填入以下段落的空格來撰寫研究的義涵或應用。

The present findings contribute to the field's understanding of the various

forces acting on _____. One such force is

_____. _____

urges _____; however,

_____. ...

A related issue concerns _____. ...

The present findings also confirm previous evidence that

_____.

Future research should investigate _____.

Finally, the study suggests that _____. This is

in contrast to _____. ...

　　此範例對研究結果的實務應用有比較多的著墨,以其研究發現可發展翻譯錯誤分類表以及改善翻譯的教學與評量。撰寫時先提出該研究發現的貢獻或所得,再分層次敘述這些研究貢獻或所得的各種應用,最後再總結出對整個研究領域的貢獻。

① The findings of this research should lead to an error taxonomy which will allow us to study the psychological mechanism involved when re-creating in a natural tongue a message originally expressed in a different one. ② They could also be applied to improve the teaching methodology in the translation as well as in the foreign language program. ③ In general, they will be useful to improve evaluation systems and particularly to unify evaluation criteria among the teaching staff of the Department of Translation. ④ On a more specific basis, this research could serve to reinforce the teaching of L1 and L2 within a Translation Program and to systematize structural and lexical contents in practical courses of translation. ⑤ Finally, we hope that it will throw some light on several issues or at least pave the way to new research projects which will help consolidate the study of translation at a scientific level.

此研究的發現應該可以發展出一個錯誤分類表,使我們得以研究以自然語言重製另一語言訊息所涉及的心理機制。這些發現也可以應用於改進翻譯和外語系所的教學法。一般而言,這些發現將有助於改善評量系統,特別是可讓翻譯系教師有統一的評量標準。更具體而言,此研究可增進翻譯系所對於第一和第二語言的教學,並且使翻譯實務課程的結構和字彙內容系統化。最後,我們希望此研究能闡明幾項議題,或至少為新的研究計畫鋪路,有助於強化翻譯研究的科學層次。

範例2 講解

1 The findings of this research should lead to **an error taxonomy** <u>which</u> will allow us to study the psychological mechanism involved when re-creating in a natural tongue a message originally expressed in a different one.

- ◎ 第 1 句先指出該研究的主要貢獻是什麼,例如此研究可用於發展錯誤分類表 (lead to an error taxonomy)。
- ◎ 之後再用關係代名詞 which 引導一子句說明此主要貢獻的應用,例如此句中即是陳述錯誤分類表的用途。

2 <u>They</u> could also <u>be applied to</u> improve the teaching methodology in the translation as well as in the foreign language program.

- ◎ 此句承接上句,進一步說明該研究發現的另一項應用,第一個字代名詞 they 就是指前句的 findings。
- ◎ 此句是用被動語態 be applied to,說明這些 findings 還可被應用在何處。

3 <u>In general</u>, they will be useful to improve evaluation systems and <u>particularly</u> to unify evaluation criteria among the teaching staff of the Department of Translation.

- ◎ 接下來再以兩個句子針對研究發現的應用作兩個層次的描述。首先本句是一般性陳述,所以句首用連接副詞 in general,而其後還有一個副詞 particularly 則是用以表達進一步的說明。

4　On a more specific basis, this research could serve <u>to</u> <u>reinforce</u> the teaching of L1 and L2 within a Translation Program and <u>to systematize</u> structural and lexical contents in practical courses of translation.

- ◎ 此句是對照於上一句，作較特定的陳述，所以句首用 on a more specific basis。
- ◎ 注意不定詞 to reinforce 和 to systematize 是平行用法。

5　<u>Finally</u>, we hope that it will <u>throw some light on</u> several issues or at least <u>pave the way to</u> new research projects which will help <u>consolidate</u> the study of **translation at a scientific level.**

- ◎ 最後要作總結，句首先用連接副詞 finally 告訴讀者這是最後的研究貢獻了。
- ◎ 句中片語 throw some light on（闡明），也可代換成 shed some light on。
- ◎ 其他如 pave the way to（為…鋪路）和 consolidate（鞏固）也都是常用的動詞片語和動詞。

範例 2 **句型**

1. The findings of this research should lead to ___研究所得___ which will allow us to study ___此研究所得的用途___ .

2. They could also be applied to improve ___研究所得的另一種應用___ .

3. In general, they will be useful to improve ___一般性陳述___ and particularly to ___對於一般性陳述的進一步說明___ .

4. On a more specific basis, this research could serve to reinforce ___特定性陳述___ and to systematize ___特定性陳述___ .

5. Finally, we hope that it will throw some light on several issues or at least pave the way to new research projects which will help consolidate the study of ___研究領域___ .

練習

請按照以上講解說明以及你自己的研究內容，填入以下段落的空格來撰寫研究的義涵或應用。

The findings of this research should lead to

_____ which will allow us to study

_____. They could also be applied to

improve _____. In general, they will be

useful to improve _____ and particularly

to _____. On a more specific basis, this

research could serve to reinforce _____

and to systematize _____. Finally, we

hope that it will throw some light on several issues or at least pave the

way to new research projects which will help consolidate the study of

_____.

3

Limitations of the Study
研究限制

論文寫到最後時，還要承認 (acknowledge) 自己研究的方法或結果多少還有一些限制，畢竟世上沒有完美的研究，充其量只有瑕疵較少的研究。因此在討論研究的義涵或應用後，可以針對研究資源不足或過程有何困難，而可能會影響結果的地方作簡短說明。在撰寫研究限制時雖然要坦白承認研究過程中力有未逮之處，多少會影響到對研究結果的詮釋和評價，但也不宜列出一系列限制或一直自我批判，反而讓讀者對研究結果失去信心。

範例

以下範例是撰寫研究限制的句型，原文分為兩段陳述兩項研究限制。一開始先表示此研究有其優點，但也有其研究限制，之後再分項撰寫限制為何。其中比較繁瑣的內容資訊則省略。

---

① Despite CAQDAS's advantages, it does have some limitations. ② First, not everyone is comfortable working with computers. ③ This "tactile-digital divide" seriously limits CAQDAS's usefulness in qualitative research. ④ Particularly challenging is the necessity to translate the analytical process into a format that a computer software program can use. ...

⑤ Moreover, learning to use the software and to analyze on screen requires a serious time investment. ⑥ The problem is compounded by the fact that relatively few people can actually use the software well, making it difficult for novices to find someone to ask for help. ...

雖然電腦輔助質性資料分析軟體 (CAQDAS) 有許多優點，但它也有一些限制。首先，並不是每個人都喜歡使用電腦。「觸感和數位的分歧」嚴重限制了電腦輔助質性資料分析軟體在質性研究上的效用。更大的挑戰還在於必須將分析過程轉化成為電腦軟體可以處理的格式。……

此外，學習使用軟體並在螢幕上分析需要投入許多時間。而使問題更棘手的是很少人會使用這種軟體，使得新手要找人協助變得相當困難。……

範例 **講解**

1 Despite CAQDAS's advantages, it does have some limitations.

- ◎ 要寫研究限制之前可以先寫一下該研究的優點，如本句先提 advantages，再說 limitations。或另如下句：

  - Although the present study has yielded findings that have both theoretical and practical implications, its design is not without flaws.
    雖然本研究結果獲致理論與實用上的義涵，但其研究設計上仍有**瑕疵**。

  也可以倒過來先寫本研究的限制，再寫優點，例如：

  - Having acknowledged the limitations of this study, we can nevertheless confirm that...
    我們承認此研究有其**限制**，然而我們也證實了……

- ◎ limitations 在論文寫作中常作可數複數名詞使用，也可代換成 restrictions, flaws, shortcomings, problems 等字。

○ 句首 despite 是介系詞，所以接名詞 advantages 當受詞，形成「despite + 名詞」；另一種相關的寫法則是「despite the fact + that 子句」。常有人將 despite 視為連接詞而寫成「*despite + 子句」，這是錯誤的寫法。另外，despite 也可用 in spite of 代換，其後一樣加名詞，如以下例句：

- <u>In spite of</u> these limitations, this method has been used to study the cognitive strategies used by native English speakers.
  雖然有這些限制，此方法仍被用來研究英語母語人士所使用的認知策略。

但也有人會因字形類似而把 in spite of 誤寫成 *despite of，這都是要注意的地方。

2 <u>First</u>, not everyone is comfortable working with computers.

○ 第 2 句順著第 1 句後面說的 some limitations，句首用副詞 first，明確告知讀者這是第一項研究限制，而且是比較一般性的論述。

3 This "tactile-digital divide" seriously <u>limits</u> CAQDAS's usefulness in qualitative research.

○ 第 3 句繼續說明第一項研究限制，語意較為具體，指出該研究主題的效用 (usefulness) 不高，動詞用 limit。

4 Particularly challenging is the necessity to translate the analytical process into a format that a computer software program can use.

○ 第 4 句持續具體說明第一項研究限制，並提出比較嚴重的問題。

5 Moreover, learning to use the software and to analyze on screen requires a serious time investment.

◉ 第 5 句轉為寫第二項研究限制，連接副詞 moreover 可提示讀者語意的轉折。

6 The problem is compounded by the fact that relatively few people can actually use the software well, making it difficult for novices to find someone to ask for help.

◉ 第 6 句繼續說明第二項研究限制，動詞是用現在式被動語態 is compounded。

◉ 句後還有一個現在分詞 making 引導的片語來說明困難的情況，而之後代名詞 it 代替的是 for novices to find someone to ask for help。

範例 句型

1. Despite ＿＿本研究主題或結果＿＿ advantages, it does have some limitations.

2. First, ＿＿第一項研究限制的一般性論述＿＿.

3. ＿＿第一項研究限制中具體的事物＿＿ seriously limits ＿＿本研究主題或結果＿＿ usefulness in ＿＿相關領域＿＿.

4. Particularly challenging is ＿＿進一步描述第一項研究限制＿＿.

5. Moreover, ＿＿第二項研究限制＿＿.

6. The problem is compounded by the fact that ＿＿進一步描述第二項研究限制＿＿, making it difficult for ＿＿第二項研究限制所造成的困難＿＿.

練習

請按照以上講解說明以及你自己的研究內容，填入以下段落的空格來撰寫研究限制。

Despite _____ advantages, it does have

some limitations. First, _____.

_____ seriously limits

_____ usefulness in

_____. Particularly challenging is

_____. ...

Moreover, _____. The problem is compounded

by the fact that _____, making it difficult for

_____. ...

Suggestions for Future Research
建議未來研究

寫完研究限制後，為了突破這些限制，未來可以從事哪些研究，身為研究者應該提出一些建議，讓其他研究的同行可以作為參考。對未來研究的建議常會提到目前的研究已經完成什麼，什麼研究還在進行中，對未來研究有什麼貢獻或啟發，還需要做什麼研究等資訊。對於其他研究者，尤其是還在找研究題目的碩博士生，都可從這段資訊中找到作研究的靈感。但作者也不要信口開河，提出一大堆與自己研究關係太遠的主題或常識性的想法，令人覺得好像沒有做目前的研究也能提出一樣的建議；另外也無需建議未來換個性別、地理區域、族群或教育程度等變項就來執行相同的研究，因為這其實也沒有太大的建設性。應該是真正依據自己研究的結果所得到的啟示或尚未完全探討完畢之處，集中一兩個值得探討的議題，提出來讓研究同儕有興趣或機會來繼續探究。

範例 1

此為建議未來研究的範例，先寫目前尚未完成、未來可從事的兩個研究建議，再寫未來研究的價值和對未來研究主題的展望。

① This kind of instruction is still very much in the experimental stage and much more has yet to be done. ② Much more also needs to be known about the way people talk and act in the discourse communities in postsecondary education. ③ This study should provide a descriptive basis for additional research. ④ There is a continuing need for an

adequate theoretical basis for the practical application of discourse
analysis in EAP.

這種教學法仍在實驗階段，還有許多需要研究之處。對於高等教育的論述社群中
人們的談吐和行為也仍有許多需要了解的地方。本研究為進一步的探討提供了描
述性的基礎。未來仍有需要對學術英文 (EAP) 論述分析的實務應用持續提供適當
的理論基礎。

範例1 **講解**

1 This kind of instruction is still very much in the
experimental stage and <u>much more has yet to be done</u>.

◎ 首句講某議題尚在實驗階段，是一種對未來研究的建議。

◎ 表達「還有許多需要研究的地方」用 much more has yet to be
done，習慣上常用被動語態。但也可以用主動語態，例如：

- ...warrants further investigation.
……值得進一步探究。

- ...deserves future research.
……值得未來繼續研究。

- Further research is necessary to explore...
未來有必要去探索……

2 <u>Much more also needs to be known</u> about the way people
talk and act in the discourse communities in postsecondary
education.

◎ 第 2 句是另一個對未來研究的建議。

◎ 表達「還有更多需要研究的地方」用 much more also needs to
be known，與上句的結構平行，仍是用被動語態。

259

3 This study should provide a descriptive basis for <u>additional research</u>.

◎ 第 3 句才寫本研究的貢獻，句末的 additional research 也可代換成 future research 或 further research。

4 There is a continuing need for an adequate theoretical basis for the practical application of **discourse analysis in EAP**.

◎ 最後寫未來需要做更多理論基礎研究來符合該領域的實務需求。

範例 1 句型

1. ___尚未完成的研究___ is still very much in the experimental stage and much more has yet to be done.

2. Much more also needs to be known about ___還需要研究的主題___.

3. This study should provide a descriptive basis for additional research.

4. There is a continuing need for an adequate theoretical basis for the practical application of ___研究的領域___.

練習

請按照以上講解說明以及你自己的研究內容，填入以下段落的空格來撰寫對未來研究的建議。

_____ is still very much in the experimental

stage and much more has yet to be done. Much more also needs to

be known about _____. This study should

provide a descriptive basis for additional research. There is a continuing

need for an adequate theoretical basis for the practical application of

_____.

範例 **2**

　　研究限制和對未來研究的建議因為邏輯訊息緊密，也常合併起來寫成一段。以下範例就是同時撰寫兩個元素的段落，一開始先略述研究的成果和應用，之後再寫這些成果中有哪些限制。而基於這些研究限制，接著寫建議未來可做何種研究來改善此限制。

① This study has demonstrated that language teaching is needed and should be stressed in translation programs. ② It follows that language training must be strengthened and better ways of organizing language courses are needed for translation students. ③ However, whether this will also apply to translation contexts in other parts of the world cannot be determined based on this study. ④ Further research is therefore warranted in different teaching contexts.

本研究說明了語言教學的必要性，而且在翻譯課程中就應該要強調。因此我們必須加強語言訓練，而且對翻譯學生提供更佳的語言課程。然而，此結論能否應用到世界其他地區的翻譯情境就不是本研究所能確定。因此有必要在不同教學情境做更進一步的研究。

範例 2 **講解**

1 This study <u>has demonstrated</u> <u>that</u> language teaching <u>is needed</u> and <u>should be stressed</u> in translation programs.

　　⊜ 第 1 句的時態用現在完成式 has demonstrated，表示從過去到現在的時間關係。

◎ 句中 that 後面所接的子句就呈現此研究結果的總結，其中用了兩個現在式被動語態的平行結構，分別為 is needed 和 should be stressed。

2　It follows that language training must be strengthened and better ways of organizing language courses are needed for translation students.

◎ 句型「it follows + that 子句」表達從上句推論出來的結果。

◎ 子句中的動詞和第 1 句一樣都是用現在式被動語態，分別為 be strengthened 和 are needed，寫作風格相當一致。

3　However, whether this will also apply to translation contexts in other parts of the world cannot be determined based on this study.

◎ 此句用表「然而」的連接副詞 however 開頭，表達與前句相對的訊息，也就是在說明此研究結果的限制。

◎ 通常論文到最後提出研究成果後，作者會把主張的強度稍微降低，而常用的方式就是降低結果的推論性 (generalizability)，就像此句中聲稱其研究結果不一定可適用在其他不同的情境中。

4　Further research is therefore warranted in different teaching contexts.

◎ 上句寫過研究限制後，本句順理就可以寫對未來研究的建議。

◎ 表「因果關係」的連接副詞 therefore 通常會寫在句首並加上逗號，形成 Therefore, further research is warranted...，但是也可以把 therefore 放在句子的主詞之後和動詞之前，如本句的 Further research is therefore warranted...。

◎ 此句中表對未來研究建議的句型是使用 further research is warranted，其被動語態動詞 warranted 也可代換成 required, needed, called for 等。也可以將整個句型改成 further research should be undertaken/pursued/carried out/done/conducted。

◎ 最後補充一個將研究限制和對未來研究建議寫在一起的句型如下：

• While this study has its limitations, it is hope that it can serve as a basis for further study in...
儘管本研究有其限制，仍希望它能作為未來研究……的基礎。

範例 2　句型

1. This study has demonstrated that ___研究成果___ is needed and should be stressed in ___應用研究成果的領域___ .

2. It follows that ___研究成果___ must be strengthened and better ways of ___研究成果的應用___ are needed for ___受惠於研究成果的人或領域___ .

3. However, whether this will also apply to ___不同的情境___ in other parts of the world cannot be determined based on this study.

4. Further research is therefore warranted in different ___（不同的）情境___ .

練習

請按照以上講解說明以及你自己的研究內容，填入以下段落的空格來撰寫研究限制和對未來研究的建議。

This study has demonstrated that _____ is

needed and should be stressed in _____.

It follows that _____ must be strengthened

and better ways of _____ are needed for

_____. However, whether this will also apply

to _____ in other parts of the world cannot be

determined based on this study. Further research is therefore warranted

in different _____.

段落指引

Acknowledgements
致謝詞

Acknowledgements

致謝詞是表達對他人指導或協助執行研究或撰寫論文的感激，Swales 和 Feak (2004) 曾將致謝詞的結構分為三種元素：

(1) 經費支持 (financial support)：先寫出提供計畫經費、合約或研究獎助金以及各種資源協助的單位或個人。
(2) 感謝語 (thanks)：再針對這些單位或個人表達謝意。
(3) 否認語 (disclaimers)：最後寫如果研究結果有任何差錯，概由研究者負責，畢竟其他人不是共同作者，無需為此論文的結果負責。

但並不是每篇致謝詞都需要寫否認語，它只是一種選擇性 (optional) 的元素。此外，作者也可以感謝任何對完成研究有直接或間接幫助的人或機構，這是一種學術禮貌，會讓被感謝的人覺得受到尊重。

致謝詞還可分為期刊論文和學位論文兩種，不過這兩種型態的致謝詞很類似，都是使用大量表達「感謝、感激」的句型，可以相互參考使用。另外要注意的是，致謝詞中作者的自稱一般都是用第一人稱 I 或 we，這樣的感謝比較直接而有人情味；雖然偶爾我們還是會看到有人在致謝詞中的自稱使用 the present author(s)，但 Swales 和 Feak (2004) 認為這種原本要表示客觀的人稱寫法，在致謝詞中出現則顯得過於正式而有距離。

範例 1

　　此範例為期刊論文致謝詞，因為期刊論文篇幅較短，只在文章的最後用一小段撰寫，而且通常只感謝贊助單位、研究同僚和審查委員等。以下致謝詞按貢獻程度分別感謝不同的人。

---

① My deepest respect and gratitude go to **Theresa Akey**, for **her** extraordinary abilities as a researcher and **her** dedication and commitment to our research collaboration for the past 5 years. ② I thank **John Swales**, for **his** contributions as research assistant to this project. ③ **James Gee** generously provided feedback on an early version of this article. ④ A special thanks to **Jeremy Munday** for **his** expert suggestions and guidance through the revising process.

我要對 Theresa Akey 表達最誠摯的尊崇和謝意，感謝她身為研究者的傑出表現以及過去 5 年來在我們研究合作上的努力奉獻。我要謝謝研究助理 John Swales 對這個研究的貢獻。而 James Gee 不吝對此文的初稿提出意見。也要特別感謝 Jeremy Munday 在本文修訂過程中所提供的專業建議和指引。

Acknowledgements

範例1 講解

1　My <u>deepest respect and gratitude</u> <u>go to</u> Theresa Akey,
<u>for</u> her extraordinary abilities as a researcher and her
dedication and commitment to our research collaboration
for the past 5 years.

- 首句要感謝的是最重要的研究夥伴，所以作者用最高級形容詞 deepest 來修飾名詞 respect and gratitude。
- 動詞用 go to 再接人名，而介系詞 for 之後接要感謝的事項或原因。

2　I thank John Swales, <u>for</u> his contributions as research
assistant to this project.

- 其次感謝研究助理，介系詞 for 之後一樣接要感謝的事項或原因。

3　James Gee generously provided feedback on an early
version of this article.

- 再來是感謝對論文初稿提供意見的人，但此句比較特別的是把感謝的人作為句子的主詞。

4　A special thanks to Jeremy Munday for his expert
suggestions and guidance through the revising process.

- 最後是特別感謝對論文的修訂提出建議的人。

範例1 **句型**

1. My deepest respect and gratitude go to ＿＿研究夥伴人名＿＿, for ＿＿人稱代名詞所有格＿＿ extraordinary abilities as a researcher and ＿＿人稱代名詞所有格＿＿ dedication and commitment to our research collaboration for the past ＿＿合作年數＿＿ years.

2. I thank ＿＿研究助理人名＿＿, for ＿＿人稱代名詞所有格＿＿ contributions as research assistant to this project.

3. ＿＿提供意見的人名＿＿ generously provided feedback on an early version of this article.

4. A special thanks to ＿＿提出建議的人名＿＿ for ＿＿人稱代名詞所有格＿＿ expert suggestions and guidance through the revising process.

練習

請按照以上講解說明以及你自己的研究過程，填入以下段落的空格來撰寫
期刊論文的致謝詞。

My deepest respect and gratitude go to _____,

for _____ extraordinary abilities

as a researcher and _____

dedication and commitment to our research collaboration

for the past _____ years. I thank

_____, for _____

contributions as research assistant to this project.

_____ generously provided feedback

on an early version of this article. A special thanks to

_____ for _____

expert suggestions and guidance through the revising process.

此範例為學位論文致謝詞，因學位論文動輒數百頁，執行過程又相當辛苦，要感謝的人較多，因此篇幅可以寫到一至二頁放在論文本文之前。而感謝的對象可包括指導教授、執行研究的場域、研究對象、審查委員、乃至於家人朋友等。以下致謝詞共分五段九句，分別感謝不同的人與其不同的貢獻。

① I am very grateful to many people that have contributed in direct or indirect ways to this dissertation. ② First I would like to acknowledge the support of **the Department of Applied Linguistics and Foreign Languages at National Taipei University (NTPU)**, and in particular Professor **Syying Lee** for **giving me the opportunity to teach English courses in her programs.** ③ I would also like to thank **all the English students at NTPU** who with **their** interest and support made the groundwork for this dissertation possible.

④ I would like to express my indebtedness to Professor **Peter Chan**. ⑤ **His** work in **second language acquisition** served as a model and inspiration for this dissertation. ⑥ **I owe most of my skills as a researcher to him.**

⑦ In addition, I would like to thank Professor **Posen Liao** from **National Taiwan Normal University** for **his** comments on the original proposal for this dissertation.

⑧ Many thanks are also owed to **A, B, and C** for **their** assistance and patience.

⑨ Finally, my deepest gratitude goes to those whose influence may not be so evident but who nevertheless provided the educational and emotional foundation without which this dissertation would have never been possible: my parents, my wife and children.

非常感激許多人直接或間接地協助我完成此學位論文。首先我要感謝國立臺北大學應用外語學系的支援，特別是李思穎教授給我機會來此系任教。我也要感謝臺北大學主修英文的同學，他們的學習興趣和支持奠定了此學位論文的基礎。

我要對陳彥豪教授的指導表達謝意，他在第二語言習得上的研究成果成為此論文的模式和靈感來源。我能成為研究者所需的技能都受教於他。

此外，我也要謝謝國立臺灣師範大學的廖柏森教授對這本論文綱要所提出的評論。

同時也要感謝 A, B 和 C 的協助和耐心。

最後，我最銘感在心的是我的父母、妻子和小孩。他們的協助可能不是那麼明顯，但卻成為我的教育和情感的基石，沒有這些基礎就不可能有這本論文。

範例2 講解

1　I am very grateful to many people that have contributed in direct or indirect ways to this dissertation.

○ 第 1 句是表達對許多人協助的一般性感謝，表達「感激」的片語為 be grateful to。

2　First I would like to acknowledge the support of the Department of Applied Linguistics and Foreign Languages at National Taipei University (NTPU), and in particular Professor Syying Lee for giving me the opportunity to teach English courses in her programs.

○ 第 2 句之後感謝對論文寫作有幫助的人，通常從貢獻程度最大的人或提供經費的機構開始依序感謝，例如最常感謝指導教授或國科會，而且會具體寫出姓名、職稱或組織名稱。

○ 本句表達「感激」的用語為 acknowledge。

3　I would also like to thank all the English students at NTPU who with their interest and support made the groundwork for this dissertation possible.

○ 第 3 句表達「感激」的用語為 thank。

○ 為了進一步描寫所感謝的人，可以用 who 引導形容詞子句來修飾先行詞的人，例如本句的句型「I would like to thank + 人 + who 形容詞子句」。

Acknowledgements

275

4 I would like to <u>express my indebtedness to</u> Professor Peter Chan.

◎ 第 4 句感謝不同機構的人，因此另立一段，表達「感激」的用語為 express my indebtedness to。英文表達感激的觀念中也隱含有「虧欠」、「承受恩惠」的義涵，因此會用到 indebtedness 這類的字眼。

5 His work in <u>second language acquisition</u> served as a model and inspiration for this dissertation.

◎ 第 5 句承接上一句，繼續說明感謝的原因。

6 I <u>owe</u> most of my skills as a researcher <u>to</u> him.

◎ 第 6 句仍是感謝同一位教授，也用到有「虧欠」義涵的句型：「owe + 事物 + to + 人」。

7 <u>In addition</u>, I would like to <u>thank</u> Professor Posen Liao from National Taiwan Normal University <u>for</u> his comments on the original proposal for this dissertation.

◎ 句首先用連接副詞 in addition，表示還要繼續感謝其他人。
◎ 句型用「thank + 人 + for + 事物」。

8 <u>Many thanks</u> are also owed to A, B, and C for their assistance and patience.

◎ 此句感謝的三個人相對較不重要，可以另立一段寫在同一句。
◎ 句中的 thank 是名詞，主詞是複數型的 many thanks。

9 | Finally, my deepest gratitude goes to those whose influence may not be so evident but who nevertheless provided the educational and emotional foundation without which this dissertation would have never been possible: my parents, my wife and children.

◎ 先用連接副詞 finally 提示已經是最後要感謝的人了。

◎ 許多論文作者喜歡在最後一段感謝家人。家人對自己的論文寫作雖然沒有直接的貢獻，卻是完成論文的重要精神支柱。在感謝完指導教授、審查委員和其他研究人員後，在最後另立一段感謝家人亦不失溫馨。

範例2 **句型**

1. I am very grateful to many people that have contributed in direct or indirect ways to this dissertation.

2. First I would like to acknowledge the support of ___資助研究或提供研究場地的機構___, and in particular Professor ___教授人名___ for ___協助本研究的事項___.

3. I would also like to thank ___研究對象___ who with ___人稱代名詞所有格___ interest and support made the groundwork for this dissertation possible.

4. I would like to express my indebtedness to Professor ___第二位教授人名___ .

5. ___人稱代名詞所有格___ work in ___第二位教授的研究成果或領域___ served as a model and inspiration for this dissertation.

6. I owe most of my skills as a researcher to ___人稱代名詞受格___ .

7. In addition, I would like to thank Professor ___第三位教授人名___ from ___第三位教授任教單位___ for ___人稱代名詞所有格___ comments on the original proposal for this dissertation.

8. Many thanks are also owed to ___其他對本論文有貢獻的人士___ for ___人稱代名詞所有格___ assistance and patience.

9. Finally, my deepest gratitude goes to those whose influence may not be so evident but who nevertheless provided the educational and emotional foundation without which this dissertation would have never been possible: ___家人___ .

練習

請按照以上講解說明以及你自己的研究過程，填入以下段落的空格來撰寫學位論文的致謝詞。

I am very grateful to many people that have contributed in direct or indirect ways to this dissertation. First I would like to acknowledge the support of _____, and in particular Professor _____ for _____.

I would also like to thank _____ who with _____ interest and support made the groundwork for this dissertation possible.

I would like to express my indebtedness to Professor _____. _____ work in _____ served as a model and inspiration for this dissertation. I owe most of my skills as a researcher to _____.

In addition, I would like to thank Professor _____ from _____ for _____ comments on the original proposal for this dissertation.

Many thanks are also owed to _____ for

_____ assistance and patience.

Finally, my deepest gratitude goes to those whose influence may not be

so evident but who nevertheless provided the educational and emotional

foundation without which this dissertation would have never been

possible: _____.

標點指引

前言

　　《論語》有云：「雖小道，必有可觀者焉」，標點符號對於許多撰寫英文研究論文的人而言就是一種「小道」，似乎無需花費太多心力學習。但是一旦忽視標點符號的正確用法，就容易導致文章的意義不清，甚至語法錯誤，讓讀者難以理解。

　　在英文標點符號誤用上最有名的笑話應屬「貓熊開槍」事件了。話說有隻貓熊進到一家餐館用餐，吃完後就掏出手槍射擊，不付錢就要離開。服務生趕緊阻止貓熊，並質問牠為什麼要做這些事。貓熊聳聳肩，只拿出一本寫作品質欠佳的百科全書要服務生看，上面寫著對貓熊的解釋：Panda: large black-and-white bear-like mammal, native to China. Eats, shoots and leaves.，有些人看完這句英文後可能還是笑不出來，其實笑點就是在最後一個逗號上。就是因為加上這個逗號，這句話的意思變成「貓熊是大型黑白相間、外型像熊的哺乳動物，原產中國，吃 (eats)、射擊 (shoots)、然後離開 (leaves)」。如果讀者看到這裡還是笑不出來，那就證明你的確需要學習英文標點符號了。正確的寫法應該把最後一個逗號刪除，成為 Eats shoots and leaves.，意思是「吃嫩芽 (shoots) 和葉子 (leaves)」。英國作家 Truss (2003) 甚至還以此笑話為書名寫了一本暢銷國際的英文標點符號專書 *Eats, Shoots & Leaves*（臺灣譯為《教唆熊貓開槍的，》）。

　　由以上把貓熊汙名化的笑話，可知在撰寫英文論文時標點符號也會扮演很重要的角色，等於是為讀者的閱讀過程中提供標示或指引 (guidance)，讓他們得以掌握字彙文意、文法結構和思維邏輯的關係；另外，標點符號也有如我們說話時的口氣，在適當

的地方停頓或強調，可協助讀者有效理解研究的内容。標點符號的使用規則並不難，只要我們多花一點時間注意，除了避免犯錯之外，還可為論文的整體效果加分，達到錦上添花的效果。

　　很多人使用標點符號時往往只是憑藉直覺和經驗，難免有時會犯錯。如果只是一般書信寫作還無傷大雅，但如果是撰寫嚴謹正式的學術論文，標點錯誤就跟文法和拼字錯誤一樣，都會讓讀者質疑研究内容的專業性和正確性，因此還是有必要花一些時間了解標點符號的正確用法。以下分述論文寫作時常用的幾種標點符號。

1 period 句號

英文的句號與中文句號的使用方式差不多，主要是置於句末用以結束一個句子，代表一個完整的語意，功能相當單純。至於其他的主要用法還有：

1.1 英文的句號可放在縮寫詞 (abbreviation) 或頭字詞 (acronym) 之後。例如：

▌ In many schools in the **U.S.** bicultural students are not only discouraged but actively prevented from speaking their native languages (**e.g.** Spanish, Japanese, Chinese).

美國許多學校中，不僅不鼓勵，甚至禁止雙文化學生說母語（例如西班牙語、日語、中文）。

> 說明 句中縮寫詞 e.g. 是拉丁文，轉成英文是 for example（舉例），而用英文 for example 時後面要加逗號，所以也有人會在 e.g. 之後加逗號。另外，通常句中用 e.g. 時，後面就不再加 etc.（等等），如 **e.g.** Spanish, Japanese, Chinese, **etc.** 就不是很恰當，因為按英文的語意邏輯，用 e.g. 所舉的例子是不需要窮盡的 (exhaustive)，也就是無需完全列舉，所以不用再加 etc. 而形成贅字。

▌ Japan has relatively inexpensive capital (**i.e.** low interest rates), and India should have relatively cheap labor (**i.e.** low wages).

日本有相對便宜的資金（也就是低利率），而印度應有相對便宜的勞工（也就是低工資）。

> [說明] 句中縮寫詞 i.e. 是拉丁文，轉成英文是 that is（也就是說），也有人會
> 在 i.e. 之後加逗號。

　　論文寫作中常用到許多拉丁文縮寫詞，都要加句號，至於要不要用斜體字 (italics) 則在不同寫作規範上有不同的意見，這兩種情況都有人使用。而且這些拉丁文大部分都是用在圓括號中作為附加的訊息，不過也有人會寫在本文中，所以沒有嚴格的規範。但是要注意有些縮寫詞是兩字的縮寫，所以需要兩個句號；有些則是一字的縮寫，就只要用一個句號。台灣同學寫作時經常不察而用錯，正確用法請看下表：

拉丁文縮寫詞（原文）	英文意義	中文意義
A.D. (Anno Domini)	year of our Lord	西元
a.m. (ante meridiem)	before noon	上午
ca. (circa)	around	大約
cf. (confer)	compare	比較
e.g. (exempli gratia)	for example	舉例
et al. (et alii)	and others	以及其他人
etc. (et cetera)	and so on	等等
ibid. (ibidem)	the same source	同一出處
i.e. (id est)	that is	也就是說
p.m. (post meridiem)	after noon	下午
viz. (videlicet)	namely	也就是
vs. (versus)	against	與…相對

1.2 縮寫詞一旦置於句尾，全句只需要縮寫詞的句號即可，不需再加句尾的句號，例如：

▌ Criteria for grouping may be the learners' proficiency in English, language background, range of interests, **etc.**

分組的標準可以用學生的英文程度、語言背景、興趣範圍等。

> 〔說明〕 句末 etc. 已有句號，不需因句子結束再加上另一個句號，而 etc. 之前記得要加逗號。

但如果縮寫詞在句尾，而句子以問號或驚嘆號結束時，還是要寫出這些問號或驚嘆號，不像句尾的句號可以省略。只是論文寫作中其實較少用到問號和驚嘆號，例如在附有問卷問題的論文才常用到問句，例句如下：

▌ Are you involved in any campus organizations or activities, such as fraternities/sororities, athletics, publications, musical groups, **etc.?**

你是否參與任何校園組織或活動，例如兄弟會 / 姐妹會、運動、出版、音樂團體等？

但如果縮寫詞 etc. 是在句中，就需要在其後加上逗號，例如：

▌ Students are also taught to utilize a variety of discourse cues such as key words and phrases, repetitions, topic sentences, supporting ideas, **etc.,** to find main ideas.

也教導學生使用各種文本線索，如關鍵字和片語、重複、主題句、支持意見等來尋找主旨。

1.3 有些寫作規範（例如《美國心理學會出版手冊》，簡稱 APA style）建議只有小寫字母結尾的縮寫詞或頭字詞才需要加句號，大寫字母之後並不需要加句號，例如 USA（美國）、PhD（哲學博士）、AIDS（愛滋病）、IQ（智商）或企業組織名稱如 IBM（國際商業機器公司）、CIA（中央情報局）等。但因目前一般學術寫作上並未嚴格要求，還是常見大寫字母加句號的情況。例如：

▎ Before the start of term two, international students will be recruited to participate in a longitudinal study on life adjustment to the **U.K.**

在第二學期開始前，會徵求國際學生參與一項適應英國生活的長期研究。

練習

請參考以下中文翻譯，在英文句子中適當的地方加上句號。

1. Horwitz et al's theory of foreign language anxiety was used as a
theoretical framework in this study
以 Horwitz 等人的外語焦慮理論作爲此研究的理論架構。

2. Translation Studies has only a short history as a discipline in its own
right, ie as an academic subject and a field of knowledge
翻譯研究成爲獨立學門、也就是一種學術科目和知識領域的歷史並不長。

3. The distribution of the degree of importance has been represented in
fig 2
重要程度的分布呈現在圖二。

4. There can be no "observation" of mental states, opinions, etc, but only
interpretation of their outer signs
我們無法「觀察」心理狀態、意見等，只有對它們外在表徵的詮釋。

參考答案

1. Horwitz **et al.**'s theory of foreign language anxiety was used as a theoretical framework in this study.

   說明 句中 et al. 通常用在該著作有六位以上作者時，此時只要寫出第一作者的姓，其後再加上 et al. 代表還有其他作者 (and others)。

2. Translation Studies has only a short history as a discipline in its own right, **i.e.** as an academic subject and a field of knowledge.

3. The distribution of the degree of importance has been represented in **fig.** 2.

   說明 句中 fig. 是英文 figure 的縮寫。

4. There can be no "observation" of mental states, opinions, **etc.**, but only interpretation of their outer signs.

2 comma 逗號 ,

　　英文的逗號比中文逗號的用法還多一些，簡單來說就是涵蓋了中文的逗號和頓號。主要功能包括標示語氣停頓、顯示條列項目和隔開句中的子句或詞語。逗號在英文寫作上的使用範圍最廣、頻率最高，也就最容易犯錯或用得不恰當。有些比較沒有英文寫作經驗的同學常在自以為語氣需要停頓的地方就加逗號，完全沒有考慮文法上的要求，這是很容易犯錯的。以下僅就在論文寫作上幾種重要用法作說明：

2.1 用單字或片語描述一系列項目 (items in a series)、也就是有三個以上的單字或片語所組成的項目時，需要用逗號將各個項目隔開。而且在最後一個項目的連接詞 (conjunction) 之前通常會加逗號。例如：

▌Audio interaction via a telephone **or** microphone brings different challenges to distance instructors, for it has a high potential for confusion**, ** chaos**, or** boredom.

透過電話或麥克風的口語交流對遠距教學者帶來不同挑戰，因為這很可能造成困惑、混亂或乏味。

> 說明 此句第一個連接詞 or 所連結的 telephone 和 microphone 因只有兩個項目，所以不用加逗號；而句末出現三個並列的名詞，此時就要用逗號將它們隔開，而最後兩個項目需以連接詞連接，例如這裡的 or，形成 confusion, chaos, or boredom。

❚ Snow, Federico**, and** Montague (2009) conducted a series of studies based on the MICASE corpus.

Snow、Federico 和 Montague (2009) 以密西根學術口語英文 (MICASE) 語料庫執行了一系列的研究。

> [說明] 此句是做文獻探討,在陳述三位以上研究者所做的研究時,每位研究者的姓名要用逗號隔開,而最後一位研究者前要加連接詞 and。如果只有兩位研究者,就不需要加逗號誤寫成 *Federico, and Montague (2009)...。

另外,論文寫作中常會用 (1), (2), (3) 或 (a), (b), (c) 來標示一系列的項目,如果是寫在同一句中,就要用逗號將每一個項目分開,例如:

❚ The procedures for writing a paper include (1) choosing a topic, (2) preparing a working bibliography, (3) collecting information, (4) outlining the paper, (5) drafting the paper, **and** (6) preparing the final copy.

論文寫作的程序包括 (1) 選擇題目、(2) 準備工作書目、(3) 蒐集資料、(4) 寫論文大綱、(5) 寫論文初稿和 (6) 完成定稿。

最後兩個項目以連接詞 and 連接,而連接詞前的逗號有時也可以省略,因為 and 或 or 等連接詞本身有取代逗號的功能。例如:

❚ The media is constantly exposing us to selected cultures, values **and** attitudes.

媒體不斷塞給我們挑選過的文化、價值觀和態度。

> [說明] 針對這種系列逗號 (serial comma)，Truss (2003) 認為英國的標準用法
> 是省略連接詞前的逗號，而美國的標準用法卻是要加上逗號，這兩種
> 都有許多人使用。筆者以為連接詞之前加了逗號可明確告知讀者系列
> 中總共有幾項，句意會更清楚。例如上句如果 and 之前加了逗號，讀
> 者較易解讀為共有 (1) cultures, (2) values, (3) attitudes 三項；如果不加
> 逗號，就有可能看成 (1) cultures, (2) values and attitudes 兩個項目。

以下再舉一例說明連接詞之前加逗號會使句意更加明確。

▌In Gile's Effort Model, simultaneous interpreting is accomplished by
the sharing of cognitive resources among four major efforts: listening
and analyzing, production, memory **and** coordination.

Gile 的努力模式中，完成同步口譯所要分配的認知資源分為四種努力：聆聽
和分析、產出、記憶和協調。

> [說明] 此句中一系列的項目中出現兩個連接詞 and 以及兩個逗號，讀者不容
> 易判定項目之間的關係。幸而句前已提到有四種努力，但讀者還是得
> 稍微思考一下才能把 listening and analyzing 視作一項，而把 memory
> and coordination 分為兩項。如果我們在最後一個連接詞 and 之前
> 再加上一個逗號，變成 listening and analyzing, production, memory,
> **and** coordination，就更加容易判別整個系列的項目。

不過如果一系列項目的最後出現拉丁文縮寫詞 etc. 時，最後一個項
目前就不需要加連接詞 and。因為 etc. 是拉丁文 et cetera 的縮寫詞，而
et 就等於是英文的 and，無需於文中重複。以下先看一個錯誤的例句：

▮ *More diverse views are heard from authors from the rest of the world such as Europe, Asia, Australia**, and etc.**

更多不同的觀點來自於世界其他地方的作者，諸如歐洲、亞洲、澳洲等。

　　正確的寫法是刪除 and，並記得 etc. 之前要加逗號，但是國內有些人可能受到中文標點的影響，想表達「……等等」時，寫成英文就變爲 ...etc.，如下面錯誤例句：

▮ *More diverse views are heard from authors from the rest of the world such as Europe, Asia, Australia **...etc.**

　　另外，此句的拉丁文 etc. 也可用英文 and so on 或 and so forth 來取代，例如：

▮ More diverse views are heard from authors from the rest of the world such as Europe, Asia, Australia**, and so on.**

2.2 兩個獨立子句 (independent clause) 若呈現對等 (coordinate) 的關係，用對等連接詞 (coordinating conjunction) 例如 and, but, or, for, so, nor, yet 連接兩個子句時，就會形成所謂的合句 (compound sentence)，應在對等連接詞之前加逗號。例如：

❚ The subjects were volunteers, **and** all subsequently completed the experiment.

研究對象都是志願者，而且所有人隨後都完成了實驗。

❚ Translation product can be observed directly, **but** information on the mental operations required in the translation process is available only indirectly.

翻譯成品可以直接觀察，但是翻譯過程所必備的心智運作只能間接得知。

但是要注意，若連接詞只是連接前後兩個單字或片語，連接詞前面就不加逗號，如以下兩句就是錯誤例句：

❚ *Radiation will be used to eliminate, **or** control the size of the new tumors.

將使用放射線來消除或控制新腫瘤的大小。

> [說明] 此句的連接詞 or 連接兩個動詞 eliminate 和 control，不能在 or 之前加逗號，正確寫法如下：
> • Radiation will be used to eliminate or control the size of the new tumors.

❚ *Sales in Japan were down 26 percent in the latest quarter, **and** are likely to continue to decline in fiscal 2011.

日本最新一季的銷售額下降 26%，並且可能於 2011 會計年度持續下跌。

[說明] 此句的連接詞 and 並不是連接兩個子句，不能在其前加逗號，正確寫法如下：

- Sales in Japan were down 26 percent in the latest quarter **and** are likely to continue to decline in fiscal 2011.

2.3 兩個獨立子句 (independent clause) 若呈現從屬 (subordinate) 的關係，而且從屬子句 (subordinate clause) 在前、主要子句 (main clause) 在後時，則兩個子句之間要用逗號分開。這種句型就是所謂的複句 (complex sentence)，而句首通常會有從屬連接詞 (subordinate conjunction) 例如 when, while, since, because, although, though, if, unless 等。例如：

‖ **Although** the cause of pharyngeal cancer is unknown, it is most common among heavy smokers and people who drink large amounts of alcohol.

雖然咽喉癌的成因不明，但好發於老菸槍和酒鬼。

‖ **If** childhood allergies persist into adulthood, they will likely be present for a lifetime.

如果童年的過敏症持續到成年，這些過敏很可能成為終身的症狀。

但若是主要子句在前、從屬子句在後的複句，則兩個子句間可以不用加逗號。例如：

▌ Obese people use up fewer calories **because** it is harder for them to be physically active.

肥胖者消耗較少卡路里，因爲他們的身體較難活動。

▌ Many students are intimidated **when** they first write online.

許多學生第一次在線上寫作時都覺得不安。

2.4 在主要子句前有些引介性元素 (introductory element) 時可用逗號隔開，這些引介性元素可以是單字、片語或子句。而在論文寫作中比較常用的就是動狀詞 (verbal) 和連接副詞 (conjunctive adverb)。

首先，句首爲動狀詞的副詞片語和其後的主要子句之間要加逗號，而動狀詞又可再細分爲不定詞、動名詞和分詞。例句分列如下：

▌ **To diagnose astigmatism,** an eye doctor will examine and test your eyes.

爲診斷是否有散光，眼科醫師會檢查你的眼睛。

[說明] 此句的不定詞片語與主要子句間需加逗號。

▌ **On hearing the news,** the researcher does not know how to react.

一聽到這個消息，這位研究者不知如何反應。

[說明] 此句的動名詞片語與主要子句間需加逗號。

❚ **When doing research for a book,** the writer usually begins in the public library.

這位作者要寫新書時，通常會先到公立圖書館作研究。

[說明] 此句的現在分詞片語與主要子句間需加逗號。

其次，連接副詞 therefore, thus, however, nevertheless, moreover, furthermore, in other words, in addition, in fact, in contrast, in summary 等之後加逗號，可讓讀者比較容易辨識句中主詞所在，而不會把引介性元素與主要子句連起來閱讀，造成理解上的困難。例如：

❚ **However,** the analysis of empirical data did not support previous research.

然而，實徵資料的分析並未支持之前的研究結果。

❚ **Furthermore,** the conclusion has been no significant difference between learning from television and from classroom teaching.

更進一步而言，該結論指出電視學習和課堂學習並沒有顯著性差異。

以上連接副詞的規則還有一些變形，就是這些連接副詞也可以從句首轉換至句中或甚至句尾，目的是為了讓句型更具變化，但仍不妨礙讀者對句意的理解。此時要注意逗號的使用，如果連接副詞在句中，通常是寫在主詞和動詞之間或 be 動詞之後，而且連接副詞前後通常都要有逗號，例如：

▌ Wagner (1995), **for example,** advocates functional definition of interaction.

舉例而言，Wagner (1995) 提倡互動的功能性定義。

▌ This distinction, **however,** seems far too artificial.

然而，此區別似乎是過於人為造作。

> [說明] 連接副詞放在句中時，其前後通常都要加逗號，不過若是只有一個單字，有些作者覺得在句中將語氣中斷顯得不夠流暢，就不加任何逗號，因此在論文中偶爾可見連接副詞在句中未加逗號的情況。

最後，如果連接副詞在句末，則之前要有逗號，例如：

▌ This does not appear to be a long-term solution, **however**.

然而，這似乎不是個長遠之計。

2.5　句子中的非限定 (non-restrictive) 或非必要 (non-essential) 元素前後需要加逗號，這些元素只是提供額外的資訊，就算刪除也不影響句中的主旨和原意。最常見的例子就是非限定的關係子句和同位語，例如：

▌ The United States has urged Japan, **which is already in recession,** to cut taxes to spur consumer spending.

美國要求經濟衰退的日本進行減稅以刺激消費者消費。

> 說明 此句中由關係代名詞 which 所引導的形容詞子句 which is already in recession 具有補述說明先行詞 Japan 的作用，是種非限定用法，該子句的前後都要加逗號。

▌ Caterpillar Inc., **another Dow component,** tumbled 4 to 52 after its earnings fell short of Wall Street expectations.

另一家道瓊成份股 Caterpillar 公司，其營收不如華爾街預期而下跌 4 點，收在 52 點。

> 說明 此句中 another Dow component 是一非必要的同位語，就算省略也不影響原句主要意義，此時該片語前後都要加逗號。

但相對地，如果是限定 (restrictive) 用法或必要的同位語，則對全句意義有重要影響，無法刪除該資訊，其前後就都無需加逗號，例如：

▌ Those instructors **who can create a warm social setting for students** are more likely to know when someone is having technical, learning, or personal problems that impede successful course completion.

能為學生創造溫馨社交環境的教師，更能了解學生何時會有妨礙完成課程的技術、學習或個人的問題。

> 說明 此句中關係代名詞 who 所引導的形容詞子句 who can create a warm social setting for students 是說明先行詞 instructors 特定的性質，是種限定用法，如果刪除則會導致句意不清，該子句的前後都不用加逗號。

2.6 句中有一系列形容詞修飾其後的名詞時，這些形容詞之間要不要加上逗號，有時並不容易分辨。通常如果這些形容詞彼此間的關係是對等獨立的，而且同時用來修飾其後的名詞時就要加逗號；另外也可以嘗試在形容詞之間加上 and 來看看語意合不合理，如果合理就可加逗號。例如：

▌ Riding's (2001) Cognitive Styles Analysis (CSA) is an **objective, bipolar, computer-based test** of the cognitive style continuum.

Riding (2001) 的認知型態分析 (CSA) 是種客觀、兩極、以電腦為本的測驗，用來測量認知型態的連續體。

[說明] 這個句子中有三個形容詞 objective, bipolar, computer-based 用來形容 test，每個形容詞基本上都是獨立平等地修飾其後的名詞，因此用逗號區隔較佳。

但若是這些形容詞之間並不是獨立平等的關係，而只是有些形容詞與名詞形成較緊密的意義單元，例如以一連串表達數量、主觀感受、大小、新舊、顏色或性質等的形容詞來修飾名詞時，就不需加逗號。例如：

▌ **Two more recent controlled empirical studies** have investigated the effects of inspection and testing on software quality.

最近多了兩項的控制實徵研究，探討軟體品質檢查和測試的效果。

[說明] 句中 studies 之前的諸多形容詞都不需要用逗號隔開。

2.7 文中出現頭銜、日期、數字和地名時，應適當使用逗號，如以下各例：

▌ After an extensive national search, Francis S. Collins**, M.D., Ph.D.,** director of the National Institutes of Health (NIH), today announced the appointment of Eric D. Green**, M.D., Ph.D.,** to be director of the National Human Genome Research Institute (NHGRI).

經過全國性密集尋才，國家衛生研究院主任、醫學和哲學博士 Francis S. Collins 今天宣布聘請醫學和哲學博士 Eric D. Green 擔任國家人類基因體研究所主任。

[說明] 英文的人名與頭銜需要用逗號分開，如文中的兩個人名後都有兩個學位頭銜，因此需要逗號來區隔。

▌ Calvin Coolidge, the 30th President of the United States, was born in Vermont on **July 4th, 1872**.

凱文・柯立芝是美國第 30 任總統，於 1872 年 7 月 4 日出生於佛蒙特州。

[說明] 英文的日期如果是以月、日、年的順序出現，這是美式英文的用法，要在日和年之間用逗號分開，如上例 July 4th, 1872。而若是以日、月、年的順序則是英式英文的用法，標準用法是不加逗號，例如 23 April 2005，不過很多人還是會在月和年之間加上逗號。另外，日期的寫法用序數 (ordinal number) 如 4th 或基數 (cardinal number) 如 4 都可以，而如果只有寫月份和年份，就不用加逗號，例如：

• An important study was published in the journal *Neurology* in **March 2007**.
2007 年三月份的《神經學》期刊上發表了一項重要的研究。

▌Nissan will spend roughly **$95,000** advertising in the magazine this coming year.

日產汽車未來一年將耗資約 9 萬 5 千美元在雜誌上登廣告。

[說明] 英文的數字如金額或統計數據，一般而言從個位數向左每三位數就需要加上逗號，以方便計數（電話號碼和身分證號碼除外）。例如美式英文第一個逗號的左邊就是 thousand，第二個逗號的左邊是 million，第三個逗號的左邊是 billion，第四個逗號的左邊是 trillion；不過英式英文第三個逗號的左邊叫做 one thousand million，第四個逗號的左邊則稱為 billion。兩者容易混淆。

▌This team of researchers was led by Dr. Brenda Penninx of the National Institute on Aging (NIA) in **Bethesda, Maryland**.

位於馬里蘭州畢士達、國家老人學研究所的 Brenda Penninx 博士帶領這個研究團隊。

[說明] 中文地名的單位是由大到小，但英文地名寫法的順序相反，是由小到大，而且每個單位都要用逗號隔開。例如上句句末先寫較小的城市名 Bethesda，再寫較大的州名 Maryland，而在城市名和州名之間要加上逗號。

練習

請參考以下中文翻譯，在英文句子中適當的地方加上逗號。

1. Successful negotiation involves decision making compromise and problem solving.

   成功的談判包含決策、妥協和解決問題。

2. The Nasdaq composite index fell 36.73 to 1896.53 and the Standard & Poor's 500 index fell 17.03 to 1130.24.

   納斯達克綜合指數下跌 36.73 點至 1,896.53 點，而史坦普 500 指數則下挫 17.03 點到 1,130.24 點。

3. The philosophically grounded framework establishes the need for (a) two-way communication (b) social integration (c) second language acquisition (SLA) principles and (d) parental participation in all classrooms.

   這個哲學基礎的架構建立以下需求：(a) 雙向溝通、(b) 社會整合、(c) 第二語言習得原則和 (d) 父母參與課堂。

4. The research design for the present study is reported below including participants instruments and procedures of data collection and analysis.

   本研究的設計報告如下，包括參與者、工具、和資料蒐集與分析之過程。

5. A robust paradigm is therefore needed to support the field in the foreseeable future.

   因此在可預見的將來，我們需要一個更好的範式來支持此研究領域。

6. The dilemma this scholar raises remains however.

   然而，這位學者所提出的兩難困境仍然存在。

7. The show evolved into a half-hour program and has been running for ten years. In addition it has generated movies comic books toys and countless other merchandise. In other words it is a pop culture empire.
該表演變成半小時的節目，而且上映十年。此外，它也推出了電影、漫畫書、玩具和無數的其他商品。換句話說，它是個流行文化的帝國。

8. On Friday January 12 2008 while driving to work on a Houston freeway Jason decided to quit his job.
在 2008 年 1 月 12 日週五，當 Jason 在休士頓公路上開車時，他決定辭去工作。

9. The questionnaire was piloted on the web for a few days and launched at the beginning of October 2008.
此問卷先在網路預試了數日，之後在 2008 年 10 月啓用。

10. The assembly plants to reopen will be a highly profitable sport utility vehicle factory in Janesville Wis. two small-car factories in Lansing Mich. and a Cadillac factory in Hamtramck Mich.
即將重新開工的裝配廠爲位於威斯康辛州詹姆士維爾、盈收頗豐的運動休旅車廠，以及位於密西根州蘭辛的兩個小車廠和位於密西根州漢特拉米克的凱迪拉克車廠。

11. Earlier drafts of this paper were presented at the Social Change Conference in Toronto Canada in July 2003 and the 38th Annual TESOL convention in Baltimore United States in March 2004.
本文初稿曾於 2003 年 7 月發表於加拿大多倫多的社會變遷會議，以及於 2004 年 3 月發表於美國巴爾的摩第 38 屆 TESOL 年度大會。

參考答案

1. Successful negotiation involves decision making, compromise, **and** problem solving.

2. The Nasdaq composite index fell 36.73 to 1,896.53, **and** the Standard & Poor's 500 index fell 17.03 to 1,130.24.

3. The philosophically grounded framework establishes the need for (a) two-way communication, (b) social integration, (c) second language acquisition (SLA) principles, **and** (d) parental participation in all classrooms.

4. The research design for the present study is reported below, including participants, instruments, **and** procedures of data collection and analysis.

5. A robust paradigm is, **therefore,** needed to support the field in the foreseeable future.

6. The dilemma this scholar raises remains, **however**.

7. The show evolved into a half-hour program and has been running for ten years. **In addition,** it has generated movies, comic books, toys, **and** countless other merchandise. **In other words,** it is a pop culture empire.

8. On Friday, January **12, 2008,** while driving to work on a Houston freeway, Jason decided to quit his job.

9. The questionnaire was piloted on the web for a few days and launched at the beginning of October 2008.
   [說明] 此句無需加逗號。

10. The assembly plants to reopen will be a highly profitable sport utility vehicle factory in **Janesville, Wis.,** two small-car factories in **Lansing, Mich., and** a Cadillac factory in **Hamtramck, Mich.**

11. Earlier drafts of this paper were presented at the Social Change Conference in Toronto, Canada, in **July 2003,** and the 38th Annual TESOL convention in Baltimore, United States, in March 2004.

   [說明] 此句中特別注意 July 2003 之後要加逗號，並不是因為連接詞 and 才加此逗號。

3 semicolon 分號 ；

　　英文的分號也和中文分號一樣，用來分開意義緊密、地位相等或並列的兩個句子。它在中斷文意的語氣上比逗號強烈，但又比句號稍弱。英文分號還有一些文法上的要求，容易與逗號和句號的用法混淆。進一步探討則有以下幾種主要用法。

3.1　分號可連結兩個語意關係密切的句子，此時不用連接詞如 and, or, but, for, nor, yet 等，例如：

▌This essay is concerned with assessing the strengths and weaknesses of Individualism and Collectivism**;** the main issue under consideration is how far these opposing ontologies disprove each other.

本文關注的是評價個體主義和集體主義的優缺點，主要討論的議題在於這兩種對立本體論的差距。

[說明] 此句其實是由兩個句子組成，中間用分號隔開，但是不可再加上連接詞，否則就會變成下面這個錯誤的句子：

- *This essay is concerned with assessing the strengths and weaknesses of Individualism and Collectivism**; and** the main issue under consideration is how far these opposing ontologies disprove each other.

上頁的句子也可以改寫成用連接詞 and 連接，並於 and 之前加上逗號：

▌This essay is concerned with assessing the strengths and weaknesses of Individualism and Collectivism, **and** the main issue under consideration is how far these opposing ontologies disprove each other.

另外也可以用句號直接分成兩句：

▌This essay is concerned with assessing the strengths and weaknesses of Individualism and Collectivism. **The** main issue under consideration is how far these opposing ontologies disprove each other.

[說明] 由此例句可看出分號和句號的功能和用法很接近，都是直接置於兩個句子中間。但用句號時，兩句的語意關係就不如用分號緊密。

從分號和句號的功能和用法很接近的觀點出發，我們還可以進一步來看用連接副詞如 therefore, thus, however, nevertheless, furthermore, moreover, in other words, in addition, in fact, in contrast, in summary 等連結兩個句子時，也可以把兩句間的句號改為分號，並把第二句的第一個字母改成小寫，以凸顯兩句間的緊密關係。例如：

▌Ethnomethodology does not deny the existence of a "common culture". **However,** the precariousness of social interaction is exactly that what this "common culture" is not.

常民方法論並不反對「共同文化」的存在，然而社會互動的不穩定性正否認了所謂的「共同文化」。

可改成下句：

▌Ethnomethodology does not deny the existence of a "common culture"**; however,** the precariousness of social interaction is exactly that what this "common culture" is not.

> [說明] 句中的 however 為連接副詞，它並不具文法上的連接功能，但可以在語氣上結合兩個意義相關的句子。原句在連接副詞前用句號區隔兩句，也可以改成用分號，這樣兩個句子看起來就只有一個句子，語意關係更緊密。另外還要注意連接副詞之後要加逗號。

具備以上的觀念之後，我們還可以綜合之前在逗號 2.4 一節中所講述，連接副詞也能置於句中或句尾的句型，經過排列組合就會形成以下六種可以相互代換的公式，請特別注意其標點符號的使用：

(1) S + V . 連接副詞 , S + V .

▌The government would allow college tuition fees to rise by as much as 18% over four years. **However,** this does not appear to be a long-term solution.

政府將允許大學學費在未來四年調漲高達 18%，但這似乎不是長遠的解決之道。

(2) S + V . S , 連接副詞 , + V .

❚ The government would allow college tuition fees to rise by as much as 18% over four years. This does not, **however,** appear to be a long-term solution.

(3) S + V . S + V , 連接副詞 .

❚ The government would allow college tuition fees to rise by as much as 18% over four years. This does not appear to be a long-term solution, **however.**

(4) S + V ; 連接副詞 , S + V .

❚ The government would allow college tuition fees to rise by as much as 18% over four years; **however,** this does not appear to be a long-term solution.

(5) S + V ; S , 連接副詞 , + V .

❚ The government would allow college tuition fees to rise by as much as 18% over four years; this does not, **however,** appear to be a long-term solution.

(6) S + V ; S + V, 連接副詞 .

❚ The government would allow college tuition fees to rise by as much as 18% over four years; this does not appear to be a long-term solution, **however.**

這六種句型雖然文法都正確，但並不代表在各種情況下使用都很恰當，尤其是第 (3) 和第 (6) 種句型的第二個句子如果很長，就不宜將連接副詞放在句尾。而第 (4) (5) (6) 三種句型都是用分號隔開兩個句子，句子間的關係相對比第 (1) (2) (3) 三種句型要來得密切。

3.2 在陳述一系列項目 (items in a series) 時，如果各個項目中已經有內在標點 (internal punctuation) 如逗號或括號時，則各項目之間需要用分號來區隔。例如：

▌Research is a process of formulating questions, problems, or hypotheses; collecting data or evidence relevant to these questions/problems/or hypotheses; and analyzing or interpreting these data.

研究是首先形成問題、疑難或假設，其次蒐集有關這些問題、疑難或假設的資料或證據，最後分析或詮釋這些資料的過程。

[說明] 此句乍看之下很像逗號 2.1 一節中的句型，都是描寫一系列的項目。如句中就有三個項目，分別是 (1) formulating questions, problems, or hypotheses (2) collecting data or evidence relevant to these questions/problems/or hypotheses 和 (3) analyzing or interpreting these data。但是與 2.1 只用逗號區隔系列項目不同的是，在這句中我們可以看到 (1) 和 (2) 兩個項目中還包含內在標點，像 (1) 項中有兩個逗號以及 (2) 項中有兩條斜線號 (slash) 以分別隔開 questions, problems 和 hypotheses 三個次項目，因此在 (1) (2) (3) 三項間要用分號隔開，彼此之間的層次關係才會清楚。

3.3 有些文法書中會提到 and 之前不能接分號，因為 and 是對等連接詞，在連接兩個對等的子句或句子時，應該用逗號，例如：

▌ A total of 64,857 specimens have been tested from 2000 to the end of 2006**, and** only 28 positive specimens were detected.

從 2000 年到 2006 年底共化驗了 64,857 個樣本，其中只有 28 個樣本呈陽性反應。

> 說明 此句用 and 連結兩個句子，中間用逗號分開，但如果用分號隔開就錯了。如以下是錯誤的寫法：
> * *A total of 64,857 specimens have been tested from 2000 to the end of 2006**; and** only 28 positive specimens were detected.

此時如果想保留分號，就必須刪去對等連接詞 and，才能形成正確的句子：

▌ A total of 64,857 specimens have been tested from 2000 to the end of 2006; only 28 positive specimens were detected.

另外，還有一種寫法也是正確的，就是將兩個句子間的連接詞 and 刪掉，把分號改成句號，然後第二個句子的第一個字大寫，只是用句號的寫法比較難以呈現兩句間的緊密關係，例如：

▌ A total of 64,857 specimens have been tested from 2000 to the end of 2006. **Only** 28 positive specimens were detected.

我們也可以用句型公式來對照這幾句的差異，它們都是正確的寫法，只是兩個句子之間語意關係緊密的程度有別，依序以第 (1) 種句型的關係最密切，(2) 次之，(3) 相對較無 (1) (2) 緊密，而其差別就是靠標點符號來呈顯：

(1) S + V **, and** S + V .
(2) S + V **;** S + V .
(3) S + V **.** S + V .

總之，兩個句子之間的連結在標點符號使用上有很多可能性。而上述 and 前不能加分號的規則雖適用於大部分的情況，但是在陳述一系列項目而且包含內在標點如 3.2 的規則時就不適用，因此在某些情況下 and 之前還是有可能加分號。

練習

請參考以下中文翻譯，在英文句子中適當的地方加上分號或逗號。

1. The Internet invites two-way discussion between people of different political, economic and cultural backgrounds however there are problems.

   網際網路可以讓不同政經和文化背景的人士有雙向討論的機會，但這也會產生問題。

2. We have only begun to scratch the surface of the daunting complexities of the language learning processes. It is therefore premature to make definitive statements about such processes.

   語言學習過程如此複雜難解，我們才剛開始探索表面一點皮毛而已，因此要對此過程下任何定論都還太早。

3. Machinery represented an enormous capital investment it could work twenty-four hours a day, seven days a week, and it came to determine working conditions. Machinery was in part responsible therefore for a great deal of unemployment.

   機械代表鉅大的資本投資，它可一天工作 24 小時，每週工作 7 天，並且可決定工作的條件。因此機械對大量失業要負部分責任。

4. You can think of this as a process of first, establishing a "universe" for your readers then, isolating one "galaxy" within this universe and finally, leading your readers to one "star" in the galaxy.

   你可將此視為一個過程，首先為你的讀者建立一個「宇宙」，接著在這宇宙之中隔離出一個「銀河系」，最後帶領你的讀者抵達此銀河系中的某個「星球」。

5. This result suggests that two-way communication is not synonymous with "interaction" it is a vehicle through which interaction is achieved.

此結果意謂雙向溝通並不等於「互動」，它只是完成互動的載體。

參考答案

1. The Internet invites two-way discussion between people of different political, economic and cultural backgrounds; **however,** there are problems.

2. We have only begun to scratch the surface of the daunting complexities of the language learning processes. It is**, therefore,** premature to make definitive statements about such processes.

   [說明] 此題第二個句子並不符合「S，連接副詞，+ V.」的公式，這是因為句子的動詞是 be 動詞而不是一般動詞，此時連接副詞需置於 be 動詞之後。

3. Machinery represented an enormous capital investment; it could work twenty-four hours a day, seven days a week, and it came to determine working conditions. Machinery was in part responsible, **therefore,** for a great deal of unemployment.

4. You can think of this as a process of first, establishing a "universe" for your readers; then, isolating one "galaxy" within this universe; and finally, leading your readers to one "star" in the galaxy.

5. This result suggests that two-way communication is not synonymous with "interaction"; it is a vehicle through which interaction is achieved.

4 colon 冒號 :

冒號通常是加在完整的子句之後，指出其後還有其他解釋、擴充或澄清之前文意的文字。基本上冒號有說明上文和總起下文的功能，以及其他用法。

4.1 冒號用於解釋、擴充或澄清之前文意的用法時，通常會以列舉方式呈現，典型用法如下：

▌ Much of this controversy appears to center around three interrelated issues: research traditions, definitions of research, and research theory and methods.

大多數爭議似乎圍繞在三個相關的議題上：研究傳統、研究定義以及研究理論和方法。

▌ Students may be at any level of competence in English: beginner, post-beginner, intermediate, etc.

學生的英文能力可能有不同程度：初學者、完成初級者、中級者等。

寫論文要列舉時常會用到 as follows, the following（以下；如下）等表達方式來引介一系列的項目或新的資訊，此時可在引介的句子與被引介的項目或資訊之間加上冒號，如以下句型：

▌ Sample items in the test were **as follows:**

測驗中的例題如下：

▌**The following table** (Table 2) provides a schematic overview of these standpoints:

下表（表二）提供這些觀點的綜述：

▌The Foreign Language Anxiety Scale was used to measure the participants' foreign language anxiety in order to address **the following research questions:** (1)..., (2)..., (3)...

使用外語焦慮量表測量參與者的外語焦慮，以探討以下的研究問題：
(1)……、(2)……、(3)……

▌Interpreting is a service which, like any other service, by definition can be analyzed from three different perspectives, **namely:**

    1. ...

    2. ...

    3. ...

口譯是種服務業，如同其他服務業，按定義而言可從三個觀點來分析，也就是：

    1. ……

    2. ……

    3. ……

4.2 寫作時若要引用其他研究對象、學者所說的話或之前研究的內容，可用冒號引介出這些資訊，而冒號之前可以用 said, wrote, asked, commented, explained, pointed out 等動詞或動詞片語，例如：

▌In her 1976 book *The Home of Man*, Barbara Ward, the economist, **wrote:** "The world's poor increasingly know that their condition is not an act of God but the choice of man."

經濟學家 Barbara Ward 在她 1976 年出版的書《The Home of Man》中寫道:「全球的窮人逐漸了解他們的情況並不是神的旨意,而是人的選擇。」

▌The teachers' enthusiasm about the project is echoed in the words of a first-grade teacher who **said:** "I am very proud to be a member of the project team!"

這些教師對於此計畫的熱忱,可藉由一位一年級老師的話反映出來,他說:「我對成為此計畫團隊的一員感到非常驕傲!」

[說明] 此句是直接引述一位教師的話,在 said 之後先加冒號,再加引號。這種用法類似中文冒號與引號的用法。

另外,如果引述的英文字超過 40 個字以上,應該要脫離原段落而另立一段內縮的引言,此時可以用冒號引介此內縮段落,英文名稱叫 freestanding block(獨立區塊)。例如為某概念引用定義或是訪談研究需要直接引述受訪者的話時,這些文字通常很長,可用一句話加冒號引介出一個內縮的段落,例如:

▌The following is a well-accepted definition of self-esteem:

By self-esteem, we refer to the evaluation which individuals make and customarily maintain with regard to themselves; it expresses an attitude of approval or disapproval, and indicates the extent to which individuals believe themselves to be capable, significant, successful and worthy.

以下是「自尊」一個眾所接受的定義：
> 所謂「自尊」是指個人對於自己的評價以及要維持此評價，它表達出肯定或否定的態度，並指出個人相信自己有能力、很重要、會成功和有價值的程度。

其他還有一些使用冒號的引述句型可供讀者參考使用，例如：

▌ Take the following extract, for example:

以下列的摘錄文字為例：

▌ The scholar defines the term in the following way:

該學者用以下方式定義此術語：

▌ Graham's checklist covers the following:

Graham 的檢核表包括以下數項：

▌ Participant 3 gives the following example:

三號參與者提供了以下的例子：

▌ One participant made the following comment:

一位參與者作出以下評論：

▌ As one participant stated:

如同一位參與者所說：

▌ As stated by participant 8:

如同八號參與者所說：

▌Another participant said:

　　另一位參與者說：

▌In the words of one participant:

　　以一位參與者的話來說：

▌This idea is voiced by participant 10:

　　這個想法是由 10 號參與者所提出：

▌Some responses are included below:

　　部分的回答如下：

4.3　在論文寫作中，冒號之前必須是完整的子句。但有些人可能受中文寫作影響，會在 including（包括）或 such as（例如）等字之後加冒號，這是不正確的用法，請看以下錯誤的例句：

▌* Two research instruments were used, including: a background information questionnaire and a learning strategy scale.

　　使用兩種研究工具，包括背景資料問卷和學習策略量表。

　　正確的寫法是刪除冒號：

▌Two research instruments were used, including a background information questionnaire and a learning strategy scale.

‖ *Early studies investigated social presence by using bipolar scale

such as: social/unsocial, personal/impersonal.

早期研究使用兩極量表，例如喜社交 / 不喜社交、個人 / 非個人等來調查社會臨場的問題。

正確的寫法是刪除冒號：

‖ Early studies investigated social presence by using bipolar scale

such as social/unsocial, personal/impersonal.

但是有時期刊論文中卻出現於 be 動詞或動詞之後加冒號，以引介出研究問題或新資訊，如以下句型：

‖ The frames of reference to be used **are:** (1)... (2)... (3)...

所使用的參考架構為：(1)……(2)……(3)……

‖ The question addressed to the students **is:** "..."

要問學生的問題是：「……。」

‖ Questions to consider **include:**

    1. ...?

    2. ...?

    3. ...?

要考慮的問題包括：

    1. ……?

    2. ……?

    3. ……?

這些冒號用法雖然偶爾會被期刊接受，但我們寫作時還是盡可能避免這樣的用法。

4.4 在論文寫作時，冒號也常用在題目或標題中，此時冒號之前就不需要是完整的子句，例如：

▌Evolution of Research in Distance Education: An American Perspective

遠距教學研究的演進：一個美國的觀點

[說明] 以上是一篇論文的題目，因為論文的題目太長，可以用冒號分開主標題和次標題 (subtitle)。

colon

4.5 論文中提到數據的比例時也可用冒號：

▌An analysis of the number of messages posted to the Discussion Board demonstrates that staff contributed 271 postings (25.4%) compared to 796 postings (74.6%) by students, a ratio of approximately **1:3**.

分析討論區上所張貼的訊息數量指出，教師發布了 271 項訊息（占 25.4%），學生發布了 796 項訊息（占 74.6%），比率約為 1:3。

練習

請參考以下中文翻譯，在英文句子中適當的地方加上冒號。

1. The sample was used in order to test the following four hypotheses

   使用該樣本以測試以下四項假設：

2. One student commented "These sessions taught me to say what I wanted to say instead of book conversations."

   有位學生評論道：「這些課程教我說出我想說的話，而不是課本上的會話。」

3. Other than informational questions about present and past teaching positions, the following questions were asked

   (1) Why did you decide to work in TESL?

   (2) What do you plan as the next step in your career?

   (3) What are your longer term career plans?

   除了問到目前和過去教學職位等資訊的問題之外，還問到以下幾個問題：

   (1) 你為何決定從事英語教學的工作？

   (2) 你生涯規畫的下一步為何？

   (3) 你生涯規畫較長期的目標為何？

4. As a student named Vincent explained

   I'm satisfied with my work. Comparing with the work of last semester, I think I am more active this semester. I participated in all aspects of the group project. And my confidence comes from the cooperative spirit of our group and the teacher's encouragement.

如同有位名叫 Vincent 的同學解釋道：

> 我很滿意我的表現。跟上學期的表現比較起來，我想這學期我比較主
> 動。我參與了小組計畫的各個活動，而我的信心來自於小組的合作精
> 神以及老師的鼓勵。

5. The majority of the participants (77.1%) were women, with a female-
   male ratio of 252 75.

   參與研究者大多數為女性 (77.1%)，女性與男性的比例為 252:75。

參考答案

1. The sample was used in order to test the following four **hypotheses:**

2. One student **commented:** "These sessions taught me to say what I wanted to say instead of book conversations."

3. Other than informational questions about present and past teaching positions, the following questions were **asked:**

   (1) Why did you decide to work in TESL?

   (2) What do you plan as the next step in your career?

   (3) What are your longer term career plans?

4. As a student named Vincent **explained:**

   I'm satisfied with my work. Comparing with the work of last semester, I think I am more active this semester. I participated in all aspects of the group project. And my confidence comes from the cooperative spirit of our group and the teacher's encouragement.

   [說明] 此段文字源自於研究對象的訪談，用冒號來引介出學生回答的內容。

5. The majority of the participants (77.1%) were women, with a female-male ratio of **252:75.**

quotation marks/inverted commas 引號

寫作時於文中標示強調、有特別含義或引述的情況,常會使用引號。英文的引號和中文一樣有雙引號 (double quotations) 和單引號 (single quotations),而中文在引述時先用單引號,如果單引號之中需要再使用引號時就用雙引號。英文使用引號的情況則不同,如美式英文的引述多用雙引號,只有在雙引號之中還需要使用引號時才用單引號;而英式英文則是反過來,平常大多用單引號,這也就是英式英文又把引號稱為倒置逗號 (inverted commas) 的原因,而單引號之中若需再用引號時才使用雙引號。而且引號一定是成對使用,必須同時出現上下引號,寫作者有時引述過長,常會忘記加下引號,需要小心檢查。以下為論文寫作時常見的用法:

5.1 使用雙引號中出現單引號的情況如以下例句:

▌ "Writing 'Writing Scientific English'" by John Swales, recounts the difficulties faced by a materials writer who lacked an adequate conceptual framework.

John Swales 的文章〈撰寫《Writing Scientific English》〉重述了一位教材寫作者在缺乏足夠的概念架構下所遇到的困難。

> 說明 此句中 "Writing 'Writing Scientific English'" 是一篇文章名,而這篇文章的主題是撰寫 Writing Scientific English 這本書的過程,因為文章名已經用了雙引號,在寫書名時只好用單引號,形成雙引號中有單引號的現象。

以上是美式英文的寫法，但如果是英式英文，就有可能是在單引號中出現雙引號的情形。例如：

▌ In Atkinson's (1998) words, 'What may be generated as "data" is affected by what the researcher can treat as "writable" and "readable"'.

引用 Atkinson (1998) 的話：「何謂產出的『資料』，是以研究者視為『可寫』和『可讀』的因素所決定。」

> [說明] 此句是英國學者所寫，在引用 Atkinson 的話時先用單引號，而引文中有特殊用語如 data, writable, readable 等字需要引號時，就只能用雙引號，形成單引號中有雙引號。

5.2　當想強調某字詞或賦予其特別意義 (special sense)，或引用某個單字或片語時，可以在該字詞前後加引號，例如：

▌ This perspective could best be framed in terms of a "container metaphor".

此觀點用「容器比喻」來理解可能最為適合。

> [說明] 有些寫作規範或英文教師宣稱句尾有引號時，句尾的標點應放在引號內。但如上句其實並不一定要這樣做，也可以把句號放在引號外，畢竟句尾的標點和引號內的內容不一定都是相同的語意單位。簡單來說，如果句尾標點與引號內容直接相關時可放在引號內，但如果句尾標點是標示全句語意時就可置於引號外。以下再援引美國現代語言學會出版的《MLA 論文寫作手冊》(2009) 上的例句，以茲證明：

(1) 問號在引號內：

- Whitman asks, "Have you felt so proud to get at the meaning of poems**?**"
  Whitman 問道：「你能了解詩的意義，是否覺得很自豪？」

(2) 問號在引號外：

- Where does Whitman speak of "the meaning of poems"**?**
  Whitman 是在何處說到「詩的意義」？

5.3 　　論文寫作時常需引用別人所說的話或之前的文獻研究成果，而如果作直接引述 (direct quotation) 時就需要用引號，並於引號前加上冒號。但引號之前除了用冒號之外，也可以用逗號。一般說來，如果引號內的文字較長或較正式，則引號前傾向用冒號；而如果引號內的文字較短或沒那麼正式，則較常用逗號。另外要注意的是，如果引號內是完整句子的引述，則引號內的句首字母要大寫，句尾要有標點。例如：

❚ One of the teachers I interviewed said, **"The** stress on individualizing in adult education subverts the group process.**"**

我訪談的一位教師說道：「在成人教育中強調個人化會破壞團體學習過程。」

[說明] 以上這句是美式英文，用雙引號，而且句點是置於下引號之內。不過要注意，如果是英式英文的話，則有可能是用單引號，而且把句點置於下引號之外。例如：

- Adler (1994) sums up the position: 'What differentiates the observation of social scientists from those of everyday-life actors is the former's systematic and purposive nature'.
  Adler (1994) 總結此立場說道：「社會科學家的觀察方式與日常生活者不同之處，在於前者的觀察是有系統和有目的的。」

5.4 相對地，如果引號內引述的不是完整的句子，而是部分的句子，則引號前不加逗號或冒號，引號內的句首字母不用大寫。基本上引述的文字是被整合至自己的寫作中，視爲文中句子的一部分。例如：

▌ An ETS publication reports that **"the** correlation coefficient between the multiple-choice and essay components of the English Composition Test is .47",** lower even than the .66 correlation coefficient reported between verbal and mathematical scores of the SAT.

ETS 的刊物指出「選擇題和英文寫作測驗申論題之間的相關係數爲 .47」，甚至比 SAT 考試中語言和數學的相關係數 .66 還要低。

> [說明] 引號中的引文被整合至作者的寫作中，因此引號內文字的句首不需大寫，逗號也放在引號之外。

▌ Ethos is understood here as **"the** set of ideas and attitudes that is associated with a particular group of people or with a particular activity"** (*Collins Cobuild English Dictionary*).

精神特質在此處可理解爲「與一群人或一特定活動有關的一組理念和態度」（Collins Cobuild 英語辭典）。

> [說明] 引號中的引文被整合至句子中，圓括號內文字是引述的出處，而句號是放在圓括號之後，不在引號之內。

▌Interviews offer an ideal platform where **"respondents** can express their own understandings in their own terms" (Patton, 1990:290)**.**

訪談提供一個理想的平台使「受訪者能夠以自己的話來表達他們的想法」(Patton, 1990:290)。

[說明] 引號中的引文被整合至句子中，圓括號內是引述作者、出版年份和頁數，而句號是放在圓括號之後，不在引號之內。

　　但是要注意，此種嵌在作者本文中需要用引號的引言通常是在未超過 40 個英文字時，可以寫在同一段落；如果是超過 40 個字以上的引用文字就應該另立內縮的一段，而且不需要加引號，這在冒號 4.2 一節中已有例句，此處不再重述。

練習

請參考以下中文翻譯，在英文句子中適當的地方加上引號或句號。

1. Mr. Thompson asked: Can anyone give an example of how we use quotation marks?

   Thompson 老師問道：「哪個人可以舉例說明如何使用引號？」

2. Another participant commented: I define training as obtaining prescriptive recommendations from a more experienced translator.

   另一位參與者評論道：「我對『訓練』的定義是從更有經驗的譯者身上獲得規範性的建議。」

3. This can take a variety of forms. One is what Glaser and Strauss (1967) call 'theoretical sampling'

   它可以各種型式呈現。其中一種就是 Glaser 和 Strauss (1967) 所謂的「理論抽樣」。

4. Word-for-word translation from L1 into L2 was found to be slower than from L2 into L1, a phenomenon known as translation asymmetry (Kroll & Steward, 1994)

   從第一語言到第二語言的逐字翻譯比從第二語言到第一語言慢，這種現象稱之為「翻譯不對稱」(Kroll & Steward, 1994)。

5. A participating school principal said: We have had the opportunity to work with and learn from student teachers, and an undergraduate participant has commented that she has learned together with the ESL students.

參與研究的一位校長表示：「我們有機會與實習教師合作，並從他們身上學習到很多東西。」而另一位參與研究的大學生也說她「與 ESL 的學生一起學習。」

參考答案

1. Mr. Thompson asked: "Can anyone give an example of how we use quotation marks?"

2. Another participant commented: "I define 'training' as obtaining prescriptive recommendations from a more experienced translator."

3. This can take a variety of forms. One is what Glaser and Strauss (1967) call 'theoretical sampling'.

4. Word-for-word translation from L1 into L2 was found to be slower than from L2 into L1, a phenomenon known as "translation asymmetry" (Kroll & Steward, 1994).

5. A participating school principal said: "We have had the opportunity to work with and learn from student teachers," and an undergraduate participant has commented that she has "learned together with the ESL students."

6 apostrophe 撇號 '

　　撇號是中文裡沒有的標點，而在英文中則常表所有格、省略和某些字的特別用法。其實連英美人士在撇號的使用上都經常犯錯，Truss (2003) 在她的暢銷書 *Eats, Shoots & Leaves* 中就舉出許多實際的錯誤例子，例如英國的加油站廣告上寫著 Come inside for CD's, VIDEO's, DVD's, and BOOK's（歡迎入內選購 CD, VIDEO, DVD 和書籍），但是正確的寫法應該把 CD's, VIDEO's, DVD's, BOOK's 的撇號全部刪除，成為 CDs, VIDEOs, DVDs, and BOOKs，因為這些物品的字尾只需加 s 呈現複數型，不需加撇號成為所有格。另外一例是好萊塢電影片名 *Two Weeks Notice*（台灣譯為「貼身情人」）也有待商榷，比較嚴謹的寫法應該加撇號形成所有格變成 *Two Weeks' Notice*（兩週前的通知）。另外還有如 Thank God Its Friday（感謝上帝，星期五到了）應該寫成 Thank God It's Friday，以及其他不勝枚舉的錯誤。可見連許多以英語為母語的人士都不見得能正確使用撇號，我們不是以英語為母語的寫作者就更應注意其用法。

6.1　英文的所有格常用撇號表示，如果是單數名詞就在字尾加撇號和 s，成為 's。例如：

‖ Part of **a researcher's** skill includes an appropriate mental attitude to his/her work.

研究者的部分技能包括對其工作的適當心理態度。

> [說明] 句中 a researcher 是單數名詞，所有格用 's。另外附帶一提的是 his/her 中的斜線 / (virgule/slash/bar)，代表「和」(and) 或者「或」(or) 的語意關係，也就是 his/her 的寫法包含了 his, her, his and her 三種可能性，這是一種尊重性別的寫法，有別於傳統只寫 his work 的男性中心意識型態。

　　如果是以 s 結尾的複數名詞就在 s 之後加撇號，形成 s'。例如：

▌ Likert scales were first developed to assess **subjects'** attitudes towards social issues.

李克特式量表起初是發展用來測量研究對象對於社會議題的態度。

> [說明] 句中 subjects 是複數名詞，所有格用 s'。

　　但如果是非以 s 結尾的複數名詞，還是要像單數名詞一樣在字尾加 's，例如：

▌ Researchers measured levels of two types of estrogen hormone in the **women's** blood.

研究者測量女性血液中兩種雌激素的含量。

> [說明] 句中 women 是非以 s 結尾的複數名詞，所有格用 's，其他類似的字還有 men's, children's 等。

　　要注意以上單複數名詞加撇號形成所有格的差異，如果用錯可能會造成語意的誤解。Truss (2003) 曾舉例說，兒童遊樂場的招牌如果寫成

Giant **Kid's** Playground 會嚇壞遊客，因為單數的 kid 接撇號所有格的
意思是「巨大小孩的遊樂場」，合理的寫法是 Giant **Kids'** Playground，
複數型的 kids 後加撇號才是表「巨大的兒童遊樂場」。

6.2 　論文寫作時常需提及研究文獻的作者，如果作者有兩人以上
時，必須先區別是共同所有 (joint possession) 或個別所有 (individual
possession)。如果是共同所有的研究文獻，則只在最後一人的名字之後
加 's，例如：

❚ I failed to cite **Bond and Dykstra's** study.

我沒有引用 Bond 和 Dykstra 的研究。

[說明] 此句指一個由 Bond 和 Dykstra 共同提出的研究。

　　如果是個別所有的不同研究文獻，則每個人的名字之後都需加 's，
例如：

❚ I failed to cite **Bond's and Dykstra's** studies.

我沒有引用 Bond 的研究以及 Dykstra 的研究。

[說明] 此句指分別由 Bond 和 Dykstra 各自提出的兩個研究。

　　另外，人稱所有格代名詞如 hers, ours, yours, theirs 等字不用加上
撇號，例如：

▎Green and Hecht (2002) described previous research of **theirs** that found a sharp distinction between the two types of learning.

Green 和 Hecht (2002) 描述他們之前的研究，發現兩種學習型態的明顯差異。

6.3 英文的簡寫形式可以用撇號來取代省略的字母或數字，但是在論文寫作中並不建議用簡寫，還是完整寫出原字比較符合正式文體的要求。以下為不當的例句：

▎*Teachers **can't** provide easy solutions to the complex societal problems confronted by many immigrants.

教師無法為移民所面對的複雜社會問題提供簡單的解決方案。

> 說明 此句中縮寫詞 can't 在論文寫作中並不恰當，筆者記得剛到美國求學寫作業時也常用 can't，但是都被教授用紅筆更正改為 cannot 或 can not，印象相當深刻。其他的縮寫詞也應該改為完整寫法，如 won't 要寫 will not、doesn't 要寫 does not、I'd 要寫 I would、you're 要寫 you are 等，這是論文寫作的基本要求。

另外要注意某些縮寫詞與其所有格的寫法相當接近，不小心就會用錯。雖然在 6.1 一節我們曾提到使用撇號加 s 可以形成所有格，但是有些所有格例如 its, whose 等並不是以撇號呈現。例如以下兩個錯誤的用法：

▎*The treatment of amenorrhea depends on **it's** cause.

閉經的治療取決於其成因。

[說明] 句中 it's 是 it is 或 it has 的縮寫，應改為所有格 its。

▌ *The study's authors gave questionnaires to 221 parents **who's** children were hospitalized for injuries.

該研究的作者發放問卷給 221 位父母，他們的小孩都是因受傷而住院。

[說明] 句中 who's 是 who is 的縮寫，應改為所有格 whose。

　　再來是數字的簡寫型式，例如西元紀元的年代寫法，有人會用撇號來取代前兩位數字，例如 1999 年就寫成 '99，但是在論文寫作上還是以完整寫出較佳。

6.4　有些文字、數字或符號平常沒有名詞複數型，但在某些特殊情況要使用複數型時，可加上撇號再加上 s，以避免與其他相近字混淆。例如 DNA's（脫氧核糖核酸）、PhD's（博士學位）、1990's（1990 年代）等；或是一個常用的片語 mind one's P's and Q's（謹言慎行），表達複數的 P 和 Q 其後加 's 會比較清楚。不過現在有愈來愈多的寫作規範建議無需再加撇號，所以上述的複數名詞就可寫成 DNAs, PhDs, 1990s, mind one's Ps and Qs。再看以下兩個例句：

apostrophe

▌ These **do's and don'ts** of credit card usage encourage healthy spending habits.

這些信用卡的使用準則鼓勵健康的消費習慣。

> 說明 英文 do's and don'ts 意指行為準則，也就是該做的事為 do's 和不該
> 做的事為 don'ts。但是 do 和 don't 一般而言沒有名詞複數型，只有
> 用在多數的行為準則時要加 s。如果 do 加 s 變成 dos，很多人會以為
> 這是一個獨立的單字，因此加上撇號形成 do's 才較易理解它是 do 的
> 複數型。不過另一個字 don't 本身已有撇號，因此複數型只要加 s 形
> 成 don'ts 就可以了。但話說回來，也有很多人不加撇號直接寫成 dos
> and don'ts。

▌English teaching worldwide threatens to form an elitist cultural

hegemony, widening the gap between **"haves"** and **"have nots"**.

英語在全球的教學帶來威脅，形成精英式文化霸權，擴大了「擁有者」與
「未有者」的鴻溝。

> 說明 句中 haves 和 have nots 因為是 have 和 have not 的複數型，具有特
> 殊義涵，因此置於引號內，而且沒加撇號。

練習

請參考以下中文翻譯，在英文句子中適當的地方加上撇號，或在有撇號的地方加以修訂。

1. The teachers expectations about their students would affect the students achievement.

   老師對於學生的期望會影響學生的成就。

2. These attitudes form a part of ones perception of self and of others.

   這些態度形成一個人對於自己和他人的部分知覺。

3. This program affects several aspects of womens and childrens welfare.

   這個計畫影響婦女和兒童福利的數個層面。

4. It wouldn't be surprising if we found higher death rates in places with lower per capita incomes.

   如果我們在平均所得較低的地方發現較高的死亡率是不足為奇的。

5. Stomach cancer is difficult to detect in it's early stages.

   胃癌在初期是很難察覺的。

6. There was a vast infusion of funding to support the development of ELT in the late 1950's and early 1960's.

   在 1950 年代末期和 1960 年代初期，有龐大資金挹注英語教學的發展。

7. Life is full of up's and down's. The trick is to enjoy the up's and have courage during the down's.

   人生充滿高低起伏，訣竅是在高峰時盡情享受，於低潮時要保持勇氣。

apostrophe

參考答案

1. The **teachers'** expectations about their students would affect the **students'** achievement.

2. These attitudes form a part of **one's** perception of self and of others.

3. This program affects several aspects of **women's** and **children's** welfare.

4. It **would not** be surprising if we found higher death rates in places with lower per capita incomes.

5. Stomach cancer is difficult to detect in **its** early stages.

6. There was a vast infusion of funding to support the development of ELT in the late **1950s** and early **1960s**.

7. Life is full of **ups** and **downs**. The trick is to enjoy the **ups** and have courage during the **downs**.

7 dash 破折號

　　破折號常用來表示語氣的停頓或轉折，可引介出系列的項目或是額外的訊息作爲補充說明。但在論文寫作中應該少用，才不會一直打斷句子的流暢和連貫性。例如：

▌ One of the implications of the study of empathy is the need to define empathy cross-culturally—to understand how different cultures express empathy.

同理心研究的一個義涵就是必須以跨文化角度界定同理心——了解不同文化如何表達同理心。

> 說明 句中破折號之後的資訊是用來進一步說明其前的訊息。

▌ Glucose tolerance—the ability of the body to regulate blood sugar levels—decreases with age.

葡萄糖耐量——人體調節血糖的能力——會因年齡漸長而降低。

> 說明 句中破折號有兩個，在中文的標點中稱之為夾注號，其實也是為了補充說明或解釋之前的文字，尤其 glucose tolerance 是個醫療術語，用破折號引介出術語意義是常用的寫法。但因為是插在句中，因此解釋完術語後必須再用一個破折號分開，以繼續提供其後的訊息。而一個句子最多只能用兩個破折號來夾注內容。

---

dash

▌We cannot expect any data gathering technique—interview, rating

scale, diary, think aloud—to serve all purposes.

我們不能期望任何資料蒐集技術——訪談、評分量表、日誌、放聲思考——
能達到所有的目的。

[說明] 句中破折號也有兩個，但是用破折號引介出的是一系列項目來說明有
哪些資料蒐集技術，其後再用一個破折號繼續提供其後的訊息。

練習

請參考以下中文翻譯，在英文句子中適當的地方加上破折號。

1. Problem-restricted theories can refer to specific problems such as equivalence a key issue of the 1960s and 1970s or to a wider question of whether universals of translated language exist.

   問題限制的理論可指稱特定的問題，例如對等——1960 年代到 1970 年代的重要議題——或是廣泛的問題，例如譯語的普遍性是否存在。

2. In other words, you cannot fully empathize or know someone else until you adequately know yourself.

   換言之，你必須先恰當了解自己才能有完全的同理心——或者了解別人。

dash

參考答案

1. Problem-restricted theories can refer to specific problems such as equivalence—a key issue of the 1960s and 1970s—or to a wider question of whether universals of translated language exist.

2. In other words, you cannot fully empathize—or know someone else—until you adequately know yourself.

連字號乍看之下與破折號很像,兩者也就很容易混用。連字號其實比破折號短,寫作時也可以將兩個連字號連用(例如 --)來代替破折號。破折號不能用來連結單字,只能作為句中的標點;連字號才能連結兩個單字。

8.1 一般來說,連字號是用來連結兩個單字,使其成為一個複合字 (compound word),可以使行文更加精簡,例如 world-class(世界級的)、world-renowned(世界聞名的)、market-oriented(市場導向的)、task-based(任務為本的)、up-to-date(最新的)、state-of-the-art(先進的)、cutting-edge(尖端的)、first-rate(第一流的)、time-consuming(費時的)、best-selling(暢銷的)、in-depth(深度的)、long-term(長期的)、cross-cultural(跨文化的)、one-sided(單方的)、low-cost(廉價的)等字。這樣的複合字通常都是作為形容詞修飾其後的名詞,但也可以作為其他詞性使用,如作為名詞的 decision-making(決策)、self-confidence(自信)等。例如:

▌ **Likert-type** questionnaires have frequently been used to measure learners' characteristics, attitudes, and opinions.
李克特型式的問卷常被用來測量學習者的特質、態度和意見。

說明 句中 Likert 和 type 兩個字用連字號連結形成一個形容詞,用來修飾之後的名詞 questionnaires。

▍A good **starting-point** is the following quotation by the philosopher

Carl Hempel:

一個好的起點是引用哲學家 Carl Hempel 的話，引言如下：

[說明] 句中由連字號所形成的 starting-point 作為名詞。

▍In the **not-too-distant** future, we shall be able to supply the answer

to these questions.

在不遠的將來，我們將能爲這些問題提供解答。

[說明] 此句的複合字是用兩個連字號形成的形容詞 not-too-distant，修飾其
後的名詞 future。

8.2 用連字號形成的複合字若是當形容詞使用修飾其後名詞時，複
合字中的名詞不能用複數型。

▍The programs would include **24-hour** customer service.

此計畫將包括 24 小時的顧客服務。

[說明] 句中 24 小時的複數名詞原本應作 24 hours，但因用連字號連結轉化
爲形容詞，因此必須去掉複數型的 s 而成為 **24-hour**。以時間為單位
的例子還有如 a **3-day** conference（一場為期三天的會議）、a **two-
month** vacation（兩個月的假期）等。

▌ The researchers describe an accident in which a **3-year-old** boy
suffered a skull fracture and brain injury during a collision.

研究者描述一場意外，一名三歲男童在車禍中遭受顱骨骨折和腦部創傷。

> 〔說明〕句中三歲的複數應作 3 years old，但用連字號連結轉化為形容詞，須
> 去掉 years 複數型的 s 而作 **3-year-old**。而另一種不同用法是在 old
> 之後加 s 形成複數名詞，如 **3-year-olds** 就是指有兩個以上的三歲男
> 孩。

▌ The device saves system power since it is compatible with both
3.3-volt and **5-volt** digital supplies.

此裝置可節省系統電力，因為它與 3.3 伏特和 5 伏特的數位供電設備相容。

> 〔說明〕句中伏特的複數名詞應作 volts，但用連字號連結轉化為形容詞後成為
> **3.3-volt** 和 **5-volt**。以度量衡為單位的例子還有如 a **10-foot** cable（一
> 條 10 呎長的電纜）、a **4-watt** light bulb（一個 4 瓦特的燈泡）等。

8.3　有些連字號形成的複合字因為使用久了，就會有愈來愈多人省
略了連字號而直接將兩字合成一字，例如 e-mail（電子郵件）已有很多
人直接寫成 email，而 non-profit（非營利的）常寫成 nonprofit、post-
modern（後現代的）寫成 postmodern、by-product（副產品）寫成
byproduct、on-line（線上）寫成 online 等。例如：

▌ The researcher's project examines the production of cultural
difference in **online** education.

該研究者的計畫檢視線上教學所產生的文化差異。

▌ All of these tests were **pre-tested** with **non-native** English speaking students at the University of Illinois.

這些測驗都在伊利諾大學以母語非英語的學生做過前測。

[說明] 此句中出現兩個連字號，分別為 pre-tested 和 non-native，其中 pre-tested 是動詞的過去分詞，因此字尾加上 -ed，與當名詞的 pre-test 不同，不過 pre-test 也可省略連字號寫成 pretest。而第二個複合字 non-native 也可以去掉連字號寫成 nonnative。

練習

請參考以下中文翻譯，在英文句子中適當的地方加上連字號。

1. Well intentioned educational policies cannot attain their objectives without creative teachers.
   立意良善的教育政策仍需要有創意的教師才能達成目標。

2. Teachers devise a collaborative, project based, multi age classroom that enables third grade students to acquire useful literacy.
   老師設計出合作性、專題性、適合多種年齡使用的教室，使三年級學生習得有用的讀寫能力。

3. Born in the deepest recession since the Great Depression, Apple's iPad becomes a must have.
   蘋果的平板電腦 iPad 誕生於自經濟大蕭條以來最嚴重的衰退期，卻成為必需擁有的物品。

4. The researcher chronicled his first hand view of the country embracing capitalism.
   此研究者記錄他對這個國家擁抱資本主義的第一手觀點。

參考答案

1. **Well-intentioned** educational policies cannot attain their objectives without creative teachers.

2. Teachers devise a collaborative, **project-based**, **multi-age** classroom that enables **third-grade** students to acquire useful literacy.

3. Born in the deepest recession since the Great Depression, Apple's iPad becomes a **must-have**.

   說明 句中連字號所形成的 must-have 是作為名詞。

4. The researcher chronicled his **first-hand** view of the country embracing capitalism.

   說明 此句中 first hand 可用連字號寫成 first-hand，但很多人會省略連字號寫成 firsthand。

　　圓括號必須成對使用，因此其英文 parenthesis 的單數型幾乎用不到，一般都是用複數型 parentheses。圓括號和破折號的功能很接近，都可用來補充其前文字的額外資訊或註釋。

9.1 圓括號一般只是補充說明前文資訊，不像破折號是用來強調這些額外資訊。例如：

▌ Woods and Keeler's **(2001)** research is one of those rare studies that provide research evidence concerning a media selection for interaction.

Woods 和 Keeler (2001) 的研究是少數有關以互動來選擇媒體的研究之一。

> 說明 此句圓括號中的訊息 2001 是前述研究者的出版年份，並非全句的重要訊息，因此置於圓括號內。這種把研究者置於句首主詞，而文獻出版年份置於圓括號內的引用方式稱為作者顯著引用 (author-prominent citation)，主要是借重研究者的權威來支持自己的論述。另一種引用方式則是把研究者姓名和出版年份置於句末的圓括號內，稱為資訊顯著引用 (information-prominent citation)，此種寫法是以資訊的內容為句子重心，引用作者姓名和出版年份僅作為補充資料。例如：
>
> • Students who take distance-learning courses are mostly female, married, working full-time, and 25–50 years old **(Moore & Kearsley, 2006)**.
> 修習遠距教學課程的學生大多是女性、已婚、具全職工作而且年齡介於 25 至 50 歲之間 (Moore & Kearsley, 2006)。

▋ On average respondents have at least 8 years' experience and interpret around 50 hours per month **(see table 1)**.

平均而言，應答者具有至少八年的工作經驗，每月口譯約 50 個小時（見表一）。

[說明] 此句圓括號中的訊息是指出圖表的所在位置。

▋ In nations with burgeoning information technology **(e.g., India)**, access to the Internet is often tied to individual wealth.

在新興資訊科技國家（如印度），網際網路的使用通常受限於個人的財富。

[說明] 此句圓括號中的訊息是舉例說明是哪個國家。

▋ In the 1960s, television **(either live or taped)** was used for distance education programs in the United States.

1960 年代美國的電視（現場或錄影）被用來作為遠距教育的課程。

[說明] 此句圓括號中的訊息補充說明是何種電視節目。

9.2 圓括號中的訊息也可以是之前文字的縮寫 (abbreviation)、頭字詞 (acronym) 或定義等。例如：

▋ Computer-mediated communication **(CMC)** has developed into a worldwide medium of communication.

電腦輔助溝通 (CMC) 已發展成為全球溝通的媒介。

[說明] 此句圓括號中的訊息 CMC 是頭字詞。

▮ *Nihon bunkaron* (**theories of Japanese culture**) has also influenced educational reform.

日本文化論（日本文化的理論）也影響了教育改革。

[說明] 此句圓括號提供了對外文詞彙的解釋或定義。

練習

請參考以下中文翻譯，在英文句子中適當的地方加上圓括號。

1. Gardner 2003 remained unconvinced of the relationship between "personality variables" p. 9 and language achievement.

   Gardner (2003) 仍懷疑「個性變項」（第九頁）和語言成就之間的關係。

2. Second language acquisition SLA theorists have struggled to conceptualize the relationship between the language learner and the social world.

   第二語言習得 (SLA) 理論家努力將語言學習者和其所處社會間的關係概念化。

參考答案

1. Gardner **(2003)** remained unconvinced of the relationship between "personality variables" **(p. 9)** and language achievement.

2. Second language acquisition **(SLA)** theorists have struggled to conceptualize the relationship between the language learner and the social world.

10 brackets　方括號　　　　[ ]

　　與圓括號同為括號的還有方括號，但兩者用法完全不同。方括號在論文寫作中主要用來顯示引文中有經作者修改或評論原文的地方，少數情況則是要特別註明保留原文的型式。這些用法較常在學術或專業寫作中出現，其他寫作型態則少用。

10.1 作者要修改原文的引文時使用方括號，其原因包括使引文更清楚、作者對引文加上自己的評論 (inserted comments)、或是更正原文的錯誤等。例如：

▌It may be true that this **[Arabic]** form of argumentation generally lacks credibility.

也許這種〔阿拉伯式〕論證一般而言都缺乏可信度。

> 說明 此句在引用的原文中並無 Arabic 這個字，但是作者在寫作時加上這個字使文意更清楚，使用方括號可提示讀者這是引文中所沒有的字。

▌As they sit on the rug, Anton picks up a book and begins interacting with Eric **[a high-status boy]**. He begins turning pages of the book and asking Eric to identify what he sees on different pages **[as if he is testing him]**.

他們坐在地毯上，Anton 拿起書開始與 Eric〔高地位小孩〕互動。他開始翻閱書籍，並要 Eric 指出書上各處的內容〔好像在測驗他〕。

> 說明 此句兩個方括號中的文字都是作者自己加上的評論。

▮ Mei Lanfang was the first Chinese opera star **[who]** went to the West. He went to **[the]** United States in 1930. So, I **[was]** curious about that.

梅蘭芳是第一位到西方的中國京劇巨星，他於 1930 年到了美國。我對這件事很好奇。

> [說明] 此句謄寫質性訪談的內容，因受訪者的英文語法有誤，在引用時可在更正文字上加方括號。

10.2 與上述 10.1 的用法不同的一種情況，就是方括號有時反而是要保留引述原文的錯誤。不論是原作者的有意或無心之過，只要引用時仍要忠於原文而呈現錯誤，就要使用方括號並寫上 sic，形成 [sic]。sic 來自拉丁文的 sicut，譯成英文則為 just as，中文則指「原文如此」。例如：

▮ The third group of English speakers are **[sic]** the growing number of people learning English as a foreign language (EFL).

第三組說英語者是愈來愈多以英語為外語的學習者。

> [說明] 句中的 be 動詞 are 是錯誤用法，原作者誤把複數的 speakers 視為主詞而使用 are，但正確的主詞應是 the third group，be 動詞應該用 is。但為了正確引用原文用字，又要顯示原文其實是錯誤的，此時就在 are 之後加上 [sic] 表示原文就是這樣寫。

10.3 如果在圓括號中的文字還需要用到括號時，就要使用方括號。
例如：

▋ We now have the Interpersonal Approaches (which include
Community Language Learning, the Silent Way, and Total Physical
Response **[TPR]**).

我們現在有了互動式教學法（包括社區語言學習、沈默教學和肢體回應法
[TPR]）。

> 說明 句中 Total Physical Response 的頭字詞 TPR 原本應該用圓括號呈現，
> 但因位於圓括號內，就需改為方括號。

▋ L2 students with different oral proficiency ratings differed
significantly from each other on the cloze (F **[2, 97]** = 4.05, p < .05).

具不同口語能力的第二語言學生在克漏字測驗得分上有顯著性差異 (F [2, 97]
= 4.05, p < .05)。

> 說明 句尾 F 檢定的呈現通常是用圓括號 F (2, 97) = 4.05，但因所有統計數
> 據已經寫在圓括號中，因此 F 檢定原來的圓括號就改為方括號。

練習

請參考以下中文翻譯，將英文句子中原本圓括號使用不當處改為方括號。

1. In Jakobson's description, interlingual translation involves "substitut(ing) messages in one language not for separate code-units but for entire messages in some other language".

   Jakobson 描述語際翻譯為「一語言的訊息不是被另一語言中分立的符碼單位所取代，而是由其整體的訊息取代」。

2. The figure of candidates who registered to take TOEFL jumped to 875,000 (Educational Testing Service (ETS), 2001).

   報考托福的人數激增至 87 萬 5 千人 (Educational Testing Service [ETS], 2001)。

3. Robinson and Others (sic) (1996) exploited this capability, using a CALL program to test this hypothesis.

   Robinson 和其他人利用這項功能，使用電腦輔助語言教學來檢驗這個假設。

4. The minor difference between mean scores for the two groups did not reach statistical significance (t (231) = .94).

   這兩組的平均分數只有些微差異，未達統計上的顯著性 (t [231] = .94)。

參考答案

1. In Jakobson's description, interlingual translation involves "substitut[ing] messages in one language not for separate code-units but for entire messages in some other language".

   說明 動詞 involves 之後要接動名詞，但引述的原文 substitute 並非動名詞，因此作者自行在此字之後加 ing 並用方括號框住，形成 substitut[ing]。

2. The figure of candidates who registered to take TOEFL jumped to 875,000 (Educational Testing Service [ETS], 2001).

3. Robinson and Others [sic] (1996) exploited this capability, using a CALL program to test this hypothesis.

   說明 此句中的 Others 不需要大寫，一般來說應改為 others，但為保留引用原文的形式，故加上 [sic]。

4. The minor difference between mean scores for the two groups did not reach statistical significance (t [231] = .94).

以上謹就論文寫作時常用的幾種標點符號及其用法作一簡單扼要的介紹，本書提供的內容大體上符合多數學科在英文寫作上的需求。至於針對某些學科更為細節或特定情況，而在標點使用上有疑問時，讀者還可以參考權威性的寫作格式規範，例如芝加哥大學出版的 *The Chicago Manual of Style*（《芝加哥格式手冊》，簡稱 Chicago style）[1] 是人文社會科學領域常用的寫作格式規範；現代語言學會出版的 *The MLA Handbook for Writers of Research Papers*（《MLA 論文寫作手冊》，簡稱 MLA style）[2] 是語言學和文學領域常用的寫作格式規範；美國心理學會出版的 *Publication Manual of the American Psychological Association*（《美國心理學會出版手冊》，簡稱 APA style）[3] 是社會科學領域常用的寫作格式規範等。但是因學科領域的不同，各種寫作規範對於章節格式乃至於文獻書目的標點使用規定就有或多或少的差異，本書因篇幅所限，難以一一詳述。另外，畢竟標點符號的用法不是一種強制的規定，許多人也不見得會嚴格遵守，難免在寫作上會出現許多例外或變異 (variation) 的情況。在此建議讀者應就個人的學術領域論文及投稿期刊規定來參照本書以及其他寫作格式手冊，當更能精進英文寫作能力，達到國際學術交流的目標。

---

[1] *The Chicago Manual of Style* 目前最新版為 2006 年 9 月出版的第 15 版，另有線上版網址為 http://www.chicagomanualofstyle.org/contents.html。

[2] *The MLA Handbook for Writers of Research Papers* 目前最新版為 2009 年 3 月出版的第 7 版，其網址為 http://www.mlahandbook.org/fragment/public_index。

[3] *Publication Manual of the American Psychological Association* 目前最新版為 2009 年 7 月出版的第 6 版，其網址為 http://www.apastyle.org/。

綜合練習

請應用以上各章節學過的内容，參考以下中文翻譯，在英文句子中適當的地方加上標點符號。

1. For example time is money you buy time save time invest your time wisely etc

   舉例來說，時間就是金錢：你會明智地花時間、省時間、投資時間等。

2. Research on interpreting originally focused on the interpreting process i e on such features as working memory human processing capacity time lag attention span and cognitive skills.

   口譯研究起初集中在口譯過程，也就是針對一些特性如工作記憶、人類處理資訊能力、時間差、注意力跨度和認知技巧。

3. The researcher is not concerned about the actual cognitive process of learning because he feels if the context of learning is properly created then human beings will in fact learn everything they need to.

   此研究者並不特別關注學習的實際認知過程，因為他覺得如果能夠創造適當的學習情境，那麼人類事實上就能夠學習他們所需要的所有東西。

4. You might argue for instance that a particular concept should be understood or defined in a particular way that it should be classified in a given way that it should be related to certain other concepts in certain ways or that it should be replaced by some other concept.

   例如你可能會論證某概念應以某種方式理解或定義、應以某種方式分類、應以某種方式與其他概念相連結或應被其他概念取代。

5. One reason why conceptual analysis is important is that concepts drive action what you think e g your concept of translation influences what you do e g how you translate But conceptual analysis is also an integral part of empirical research. It involves processes like the following

概念分析很重要的一個原因就是概念可驅動行為：你所想的（例如你對翻譯的概念）會影響你所做的（例如你如何翻譯）。但是概念分析也是實徵研究的一部分，它所涉及的過程如下：

6. Although ESL students usually have opportunities to interact with clerks in the market, bus drivers, etc when it comes to discussing real issues, values and experiences they are often limited to exchanges with compatriots in their native tongue.

雖然以英語為第二語言的學生通常有機會與市場員工、公車司機等人互動，但是當討論真正的議題、價值觀和經驗時，他們通常只限於與說母語的同胞交談。

7. As you grow up this unconscious image of the ideal sweetheart gradually takes shape. You imagine exactly how your true love will look his or her hair and eye color, and height and weight as well as personality manners and other features.

在你成長過程中，這個理想伴侶的無意識形象也會逐漸成形。你會想像愛人的外貌——他／她的頭髮和眼睛顏色、身高和體重——以及其個性、態度和其他特質。

8. Likert scale questionnaires are not the only option available to
   researchers measuring respondents characteristics attitudes or
   opinions. Interviews based on well planned open ended questions can
   also be considered informative.

   李克特式量表問卷並不是研究者測量應答者特質、態度和意見的唯一選
   擇。設計良好之開放性問題的訪談也能取得很多資訊。

9. Scholar Orville Schell wrote in a column It is unsettling to realize that
   if the West cannot quickly straighten out its systems of government
   only politically unreformed states like China will be able to make the
   decisions that a nation needs to survive in todays high speed high
   tech increasingly globalized world.

   學者 Orville Schell 在專欄中寫道:「想到以下的說法就令人不安,亦即如
   果西方無法盡快改善其政府體系,反而只有像中國這種未經政治改革的國
   家才能做出決策,使國家能在今日快速、高科技和日益全球化的世界中生
   存。」

10. In addition I delete from the profile certain characteristics of oral
    speech that a participant would not use in writing for example
    repetitious uhms, ahs, you knows, and other idiosyncrasies.

    除此之外,我從人物側寫中刪除參與者不會在書面文本中使用的一些口語
    特徵——例如反覆說些「嗯」、「啊」、「這個嘛」以及其他特別用語。

參考答案

1. For example, time is money: you buy time, save time, invest your time wisely, etc.

2. Research on interpreting originally focused on the interpreting process, i.e. on such features as working memory, human processing capacity, time lag, attention span and cognitive skills.

3. The researcher is not concerned about the actual cognitive process of learning because, he feels, if the context of learning is properly created, then human beings will, in fact, learn everything they need to.

4. You might argue, for instance, that a particular concept should be understood or defined in a particular way; that it should be classified in a given way; that it should be related to certain other concepts in certain ways; or that it should be replaced by some other concept.

5. One reason why conceptual analysis is important is that concepts drive action: what you think (e.g. your concept of translation) influences what you do (e.g. how you translate). But conceptual analysis is also an integral part of empirical research. It involves processes like the following:

6. Although ESL students usually have opportunities to interact with clerks in the market, bus drivers, etc., when it comes to discussing real issues, values, and experiences, they are often limited to exchanges with compatriots in their native tongue.

7. As you grow up, this unconscious image of the ideal sweetheart gradually takes shape. You imagine exactly how your true love will look—his or her hair and eye color, and height and weight—as well as personality, manners, and other features.

8. Likert-scale questionnaires are not the only option available to researchers measuring respondents' characteristics, attitudes, or opinions. Interviews based on well-planned, open-ended questions can also be considered informative.

9. Scholar Orville Schell wrote in a column, "It is unsettling to realize that, if the West cannot quickly straighten out its systems of government, only politically unreformed states like China will be able to make the decisions that a nation needs to survive in today's high-speed, high-tech, increasingly globalized world."

10. In addition, I delete from the profile certain characteristics of oral speech that a participant would not use in writing—for example, repetitious "uhms," "ahs," "you knows," and other idiosyncrasies.

   [說明] 美式英文較常把逗號放在引號內，如本句中的 "uhms," "ahs," "you knows,"，而且這些字都是字尾加 s 的複數名詞。

參考書目 (References)

Aaron, J. E. (2005). *The little, brown essential handbook* (5th ed.). Upper Saddle River, NJ: Pearson.

Angelelli, G. V. (2006). Validating professional standards and codes: challenges and opportunities. *Interpreting, 8*(2), 175-193.

Barbara, K., & Nespoulous, J.-L. (2006). Working memory performance in expert and novice interpreters. *Interpreting, 8*(1), 14.

Baugh, L. S. (1997). *How to write term papers and reports* (2nd ed.). Chicago: VGM Career Horizons.

Biber, D., Johansson, S., Leech, G., Conrad, S., & Finegan, E. (1999). *Longman grammar of spoken and written English.* Harlow, Essex: Pearson Education.

Bowker, L. (2001). Toward a methodology for a corpus-based approach to translation evaluation. *Meta, XLVI*(2), 345-364.

Boyle, R. (1996). Modelling oral presentations. *ELT Journal, 50*(2), 115-126.

Brown, D. (2007). *Principles of Language Learning and Teaching* (5th ed.). White Plains, NY: Pearson Education.

Chang, C.-c., & Schallert, D., L. (2007). The impact of directionality on Chinese/English simultaneous interpreting. *Interpreting, 9*(2), 137-176.

Chiang, Y.-n. (2009). Foreign language anxiety in Taiwanese student interpreters. *Meta, LIV*(3), 605-621.

Chou, Y., & Liao, P. (2008). College teacher' beliefs about the use of CALL to teach English. *Studies in English Language and Literature, 22,* 59-79.

Colina, S. (2003). *Translation teaching, from research to the classroom: a handbook for teachers.* Boston: McGraw-Hill.

Gall, J. P., Gall, M. D., & Borg, W. R. (1999). *Applying educational research: a practical guide* (4th ed.). New York: Addison Wesley Longman.

Gibaldi, J. (2009). *MLA handbook for writers of research papers* (7th ed.). New York: Modern Language Association.

Green, S. B., Salkind, N. J., & Akey, T. M. (2000). *Using SPSS for Windows: analyzing and understanding data* (2nd ed.). Upper Saddle River, NJ: Prentice Hall.

Haswell, R. (1991). *Gaining ground in college writing: tales of development and interpretation.* Dallas: Southern Methodist University Press.

Hewings, M. (2004). An 'important contribution' or 'tiresome reading'? A study of evaluation in peer reviews of journal article submissions. *Journal of Applied Linguistics, 1*(3), 247-274.

Horwitz, E. K. (1987). Surveying student beliefs about language learning. In A. L. Wenden & J. Rubin (Eds.), *Learner strategies in language learning* (pp. 119-129). Englewood Cliffs, NJ: Prentice-Hall.

Huckin, T. N., & Olsen, L. A. (1991). *Technical writing and professional communication for nonnative speakers of English* (International ed.). Singapore: McGraw-Hill.

Hyland, K. (2008). Academic clusters: text patterning in published and postgraduate writing. *International Journal of Applied Linguistics, 18*(1), 41-62.

Kiraly, D. C. (2000). *A social constructivist approach to translator education.* Manchester, UK: St. Jerome.

Kopke, B., & Nespoulous, J.-L. (2006). Working memory performance in expert and novice interpreters. *Interpreting, 8*(1), 1-23.

Kramer, M., Leggett, G., & D., M. C. (1995). *Prentice Hall handbook for writers* (12th ed.). Englewood Cliffs, NJ: Prentice Hall.

Lee, J. (2007). Telephone interpreting: seen from the interpreters' perspective. *Interpreting, 9*(2), 231-252.

Lewis, M. (2002). *Implementing the lexical approach.* Boston: Heinle.

Li, D. (2002). Translator training: what translation students have to say. *META, 47*(4), 513-531.

Li, D. (2007). Translation curriculum and pedagogy. *Target, 19*(1), 105-133.

McKenna, E. (1987). Preparing foreign students to enter discourse communities in the U.S. *English for Specific Purpose, 6*(3), 187-202.

MLA Handbook for Writers of Research Papers (7th ed.). New York. Modern Language Association.

Publication Manual of the American Psychological Association (6th ed.). Washington, DC: American Psychological Association.

Ragonis, N., & Ben-Ari, M. (2005). A long-term investigation of the comprehension of OOP concepts by novices. *Computer Science Education, 15*(3), 203-221.

Raimes, A. (1998). *Grammar troublespots* (2nd ed.). Cambridge: Cambridge University Press.

Rudestam, K. E., & Newton, R. R. (2001). *Surviving your dissertation* (2nd ed.). Thousand Oak, CA: Sage.

Schaffner, C. (2004). Researching translation and interpreting. In C. Schaffner (Ed.), *Translation research and interpreting research: traditions, gaps and synergies* (pp. 1-9). Clevedon: Multilingual Matters.

Scott, M. (1996). *Wordsmith Tools 4*. Oxford: Oxford University Press.

Shaw, H. (1963). *Punctuate it right*. New York: Harper & Row.

Shi, L. (2002). How Western-trained Chinese TESOL professionals publish in their home environment. *TESOL Quarterly, 36*(4), 625-634.

Slade, C. (2000). *Form & style* (12th ed.). Boston: Houghton Mifflin.

Strunk, W., & White, E. B. (1979). *The elements of styles* (3rd ed.). New York: Macmillan.

Swales, J. M., & Feak, C. B. (2004). *Academic writing for graduate students* (2nd ed.). Ann Arbor: MI: The University of Michigan Press.

Swan, M. (1992). *Practical English usage*. Oxford: Oxford University Press.

TESOL (2006). *TESOL Quarterly back issues 1967-2005* [CD-ROM]. Taichung: QBook.

Truss, L. (2003). *Eats, shoots & leaves: the zero tolerance approach to punctuation*. New York: Gotham.

Weissberg, R., & Buker, S. (1990). *Writing up research*. Englewood Cliffs, NJ: Prentice-Hall.

Wenden, A. (1987). How to be a successful language learner: Insights and prescriptions from L2 learners. In A. Wenden & J. Rubin (Eds.), *Learner strategies in language learning* (pp. 103-118). Englewood Cliffs, NJ: Prentice-Hall.

國家圖書館出版品預行編目資料

英文研究論文寫作──段落指引 / 廖柏森作 .
　　-- 初版 . -- 臺北市：象文圖書 , 民 99. 09
　　面；公分

ISBN 978-957-532-388-2

1. 英語　2. 論文寫作法

805.175　　　　　　　　　　　　　　　99015024

定價 450 元

英文研究論文寫作——段落指引

中華民國九十九年九月　初版一刷

作　　者	廖柏森
主　　編	陳瑠琍
編　　輯	黃炯睿
美術設計	嚴國綸
發 行 人	黃建和
發 行 所	眾文圖書股份有限公司
	台北市重慶南路一段 9 號
網路書店	http://www.jwbooks.com.tw
電　　話	(02) 2311-8168
傳　　真	(02) 2311-9683
劃撥帳號	01048805

局版台業字第 1593 號　　　　　　　　　　　　　　　　版權所有・請勿翻印

本書若有缺頁、破損或裝訂錯誤，請寄回下列地址更換。

台北縣 231 新店市寶橋路 235 巷 6 弄 2 號 4 樓